CASE REPORT:

REPORTING OFFICER: PIGHEADSKI

YOUR REF: 8703/K9990/SLEEZE

MY REF: that guy in black and white

STATEMENT (*press hard – you are making nine copies*):

Evidence clearly shows the individuals **CARNELL, JOHN** and **LANNING, ANDY** to be the masterminds behind the whole turkey shoot. This officer believes they planned the thing together at a series of high-level meetings before **CARNELL** wrote the whole thing down. It's my contention that **LANNING** then drew up blueprints for the scheme from **CARNELL**'s notes. Up until the start of the second case (the so called '*Reel to Real*' scam) it is believed suspect **HINE, DAVE** collaborated with **LANNING** on the blueprint work. After that point we believe **BASKERVILLE, STEPHEN** took over and was connected to the affair until the end. **WHITE, STEVE**, who has been taken in on several other hue offences, has now been positively identified as the team's 'colour-man' throughout. **STONE, HELEN** is wanted for questioning in respect of a number of calligraphic crimes that took place from the third case ('*Murder in Space*' so-called) onwards. This officer would also like to talk to **BAMBOS**, who has several previous lettering convictions. The word on the streets say that **CARNELL** and **LANNING** themselves were working on the say-so of **ABNETT, DAN** and his assistant **PAPP, JACQUI**. This is subject to confirmation, but this officer is keen to interview known associates **STARKINGS, RICHARD, HEATH, SOPHIE, HIGGINS, JOHN** and **WILLIAMS, ANTHONY** about their not inconsiderable part in this diabolical crime. This file was produced under cross-examination by **McCORMACK, CHRISTINA.**

THE SLEEZE BROTHERS™ Published by MARVEL COMICS LTD 13-15 Arundel Street, London WC2. THE SLEEZE BROTHERS copyright © 1990 John Carnell and Andy Lanning. All rights reserved. No part of this book may be printed or reproduced in any manner whatsoever without written permission of the authors and the publisher. THE SLEEZE BROTHERS and all prominent characters appearing in this book are trademarks of John Carnell and Andy Lanning. Printed in England. ISBN No. 1 85400 242 2

PIGHEADSKI: SERGEANT PEGHEADSKI CONDUCTING INTERROGATION OF SUBJECTS **SLEEZE, EL APE** AND **SLEEZE, DEADBEAT.** CORRECT PROCEDURE HAS BEEN OBSERVED IN ALL ASPECTS DURING PREPARATION FOR INTERVIEW: SUBJECTS HAVE BEEN INFORMED OF THEIR RIGHTS, A BRIGHT LIGHT HAS BEEN ARRANGED TO SHINE IN THEIR FACES, THIS OFFICER HAS ROLLED UP HIS SHIRTSLEEVES AND FILLED AN ASHTRAY WITH CIGGIE BUTTS TO LEND A WEARY, WORK-A-DAY ATMOSPHERE TO THE EVENT AND MY ASSISTANT SCRATCHINGS IS WAITING OUTSIDE TO COME IN AND DO THE 'NICE GUY' BIT WHEN THE TIME COMES. THERE IS NO ONE IN SCREAMING DISTANCE. JUST ME, SCRATCHINGS, THE (expletive deleted) SLEEZES AND THAT (three expletives and rude gesture deleted) RECORDING MACHINE.

SUBJECT EL APE (at low volume): REMEMBER BRO, DENY *EVERYTHING.*

SUBJECT DEADBEAT: YUP.

PIGHEADSKI: WHAT WAS THAT? WHAT WERE YOU MUTTER-ING ABOUT? EH?

SUBJECT EL APE: NOTHING.

SUBJECT DEADBEAT: WE WERN'T EVEN MUTTERING.

PIGHEADSKI: WELL . . . YOU SLEEZES . . . LET'S GET THIS THING ON THE ROAD . . . FIRST QUESTION: HAVE YOU EVER SEEN THIS BEFORE?

(Conducting officer produces exhibit 'Q')

SUBJECT EL APE: ER . . . NO.

SUBJECT DEADBEAT: SEEN WHAT?

PIGHEADSKI: THIS! THIS THING I'M HOLDING IN MY HANDS! IS IT YOURS?

SUBJECT EL APE: ABSOLUTELY NOT.

SUBJECT DEADBEAT: HAND?

SUBJECT EL APE: (low volume): DON'T OVER DO IT!

PIGHEADSKI: THIS! THIS! THIS! THIS IS A KODIK HOLOMATIC 70 MIL TELEPHOTON CAMERA.

SUBJECT DEADBEAT: NO, IT ISN'T.

PIGHEADSKI: YES IT (expletive deleted) IS! AND WHAT'S MORE, I HAVE REASON TO BELIEVE YOU HAVE SEEN IT BEFORE BECAUSE IT'S YOURS!

SUBJECT DEADBEAT: DEFINITELY ISN'T.

SUBJECT EL APE: I AGREE WITH HIM.

PIGHEADSKI: I DISAGREE WITH BOTH OF YOU! IT *IS* YOURS! IT'S GOT YOUR (expletive deleted) DABS ALL OVER IT!

SUBJECT EL APE: OH . . . A *KODIK* DID YOU SAY? OH WELL, THEN . . . YES IT IS OURS. DEFINITELY IS. YUP.

SUBJECT DEADBEAT: ISN'T.

PIGHEADSKI: SHUT UP, YOU. IT IS MY CONTENTION THAT WITH THIS VERY CAMERA, YOU TWO INDULGED IN A PHOTOGRAPHIC CAMPAIGN OF THE VOYEURISTIC TYPE

AND TOOK, WITHOUT THE PERMISSION OF ANY PARTY INVOLVED AT ANY POINT, TOTALLY GROSS SNAPS OF KINKY ALIEN SEX!

SUBJECT EL APE: KINKY ALIEN SEX? US?

PIGHEADSKI: THAT'S *KINKY ALIEN SEX* AS SET DOWN IN PARAGRAPH 186 OF THE MANUAL OF *PROHIBITED INTER-SPECIES HIGH-JINKS.* LOOK AT THIS CHARGE SHEET: NINETEEN COUNTS OF BREAKING AND ENTERING, FIFTY SEVEN COUNTS OF PHOTOGRAPHING PRIVATE PARTS WITHOUT THE OWNER'S WRITTEN PERMISSION, THIRTY ONE COUNTS OF ENTERING, BREAKING AND TRYING TO STICK BACK TOGETHER WITH GLUE, SIX COUNTS OF COMPLETE STUPIDITY ON A PUBLIC FIRE-ESCAPE, AND NINE COUNTS OF LOOKING THROUGH WINDOWS WITH AN INTENT TO BE NAUGHTY. YOU SORRY PAIR OF (unusual expletive deleted, but stored in memory for future consideration).

SUBJECT EL APE: WE WERE INVESTIGATING SOME ADULTERY CASES FOR CLIENTS. WE'RE PRIVATE DICKS. IT'S OUR JOB. IT'S NOT AGAINST THE LAW.

SUBJECT DEADBEAT: YES, IT IS.

SUBJECT EL APE: NO, IT'S NOT! WE'RE PROFESSIONALS. WE GOT PAID TO DO IT.

PIGHEADSKI: PAID? HOW MANY TIMES.

SUBJECT EL APE: A DOZEN OR SO . . .

PIGHEADSKI: SO I ADD A DOZEN COUNTS OF UNDECLARED EARNINGS FROM AN IMMORAL AND NAUSEATING SOURCE TO THE CHARGE SHEET.

SUBJECT EL APE: WHY YOU . . . YOU'RE A (six expletives deleted), YOU KNOW THAT DON'T YOU?

SUBJECT DEADBEAT: NO, HE'S NOT.

PIGHEADSKI: OKAY . . . WHAT ABOUT THIS GUY? RECOG-NISE HIS FACE?

(Conducting officer shows subject photo-fit KF172 6A)

SUBJECT EL APE: NO.

SUBJECT DEADBEAT: NOPE.

PIGHEADSKI: TRY HARDER. THIS IS THE NOTORIOUS SICILLICON SUPERGRASS WHO WENT MISSING A COUPLE OF HOURS BEFORE THE BIG SHOW TRIAL A WHILE BACK. I CONTEND THAT YOU WERE THE LAST PERSONS TO SEE HIM ALIVE AND THE FIRST TO SEE HIM DEAD.

SUBJECT EL APE: NO NO NO NO NO NO NO NO NO. ABSOLUTELY NOT.

SUBJECT DEADBEAT: I CONTEND THAT YOU ARE NOT RIGHT ABOUT THAT.

PIGHEADSKI: THAT'S INTERFERING WITH A FEDERAL WITNESS, CONSIPIRACY TO CAUSE A THREE MEGATON EXPLOSION IN THE DOWNPLATFORM AREA, DRIVING A HOVER VEHICLE IN A BUILT-UP AREA WITH YOUR EYES SHUT . . .

SUBJECT EL APE: YOU'RE MAKING IT UP. WE NEVER DID THAT.

PIGHEADSKI: IT'LL STICK, DON'T WORRY.

SUBJECT DEADBEAT: NO, IT WON'T.

PIGHEADSKI (series of expletives lasting thirty nine point four seconds deleted. Coherent content of sentence minimal. Only non-censorable word identifiable 'IN', 'BASEBALL BAT', 'YODEL' and 'MULE' and frankly, this unit is a bit worried about the 'MULE'.)

SUBJECT EL APE: THIS IS THE 'NICE GUY - NASTY GUY' ROUTINE, ISN'T IT?

SUBJECT DEADBEAT: NO.

SUBJECT EL APE: IS THE NICE GUY OUTSIDE WAITING TO COME IN AND GIVE US CANDY? IS HE? IS HE? IS HE REALLY NICE? COULD HE GET US SOME COFFEE AND OTHER STUFF? I'M ABOUT READY FOR THE NICE GUY BIT, YOU KNOW. YOU HAVE TO HAVE BALANCE . . .

PIGHEADSKI: I'M THE NICE GUY

(Ninety four seconds silence)

SUBJECT EL APE: OH.

PIGHEADSKI: SO LET'S LOOK AT SOME OTHER STUFF, SHALL WE? THE FLOTEL FIASCO? YOUR INVOLVEMENT IN THE REEL TO REAL AFFAIR? THAT BUSINESS AT THE WIMP BUILDING? AT THE PHONEY AWARDS CEREMONY? HOW LONG HAVE YOU KNOWN MARILYN BLONDECLONE? DO YOU OFTEN ASSOCIATE WITH KNOWN SCOOPERS? WHO IS THE BUGGER? WHY DOES VANITY CASE HATE YOU SO, SO SO MUCH? WELL?

SUBJECT EL APE: WHAT DO YOU WANT ME TO ANSWER FIRST?

PIGHEADSKI: WORK THROUGH THEM. LET'S REVIEW YOUR ENTIRE FILE, SHALL WE?

SUBJECT DEADBEAT: YOU'RE NOT REALLY THE NICE GUY, ARE YOU?

(Conducting officer leaves interrogation suite. Muffled noises heard from corridor. Conducting officer returns to suite with bruises on foreheads).

PIGHEADSKI: STENOGRAPHER UNIT? WE'LL FINISH THIS SESSION LATER WHEN I'VE TAKEN SOME PAIN-AWAY AND HAD A LIE DOWN.

THIS UNIT: WANT ME TO READ IT BACK TO YOU NOW?

PIGHEADSKI: DON'T YOU (expletive deleted) DARE, YOU (seven expletives deleted) MACHINE.

(Conducting officer leaves interrogation suite).

SUBJECT EL APE: WELL, I THOUGHT THAT ACTUALLY WENT QUITE WELL, DIDN'T YOU?

TRANSCRIPT ENDS . . . .

7

8

THIS IS IT, EL APE...BUT BEFORE WE GO ANY FURTHER, I THINK I SHOULD *EXPLAIN*...

NO, *NO*... YOU'VE DONE ENOUGH, MY GOOD BROTHER...THIS PLACE IS *PERFECT!* REAL *SLEAZY*...REAL *BOGART!*

I *KNEW* YOU WOULDN'T LET ME DOWN...IT'S JUST LIKE IN THE OLD MOVIES I WATCHED ON THE RIM...

BUT, EL APE... *LISTEN!*

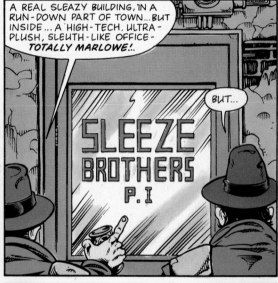

A REAL SLEAZY BUILDING, IN A RUN-DOWN PART OF TOWN...BUT INSIDE...A HIGH-TECH, ULTRA-PLUSH, SLEUTH-LIKE OFFICE— *TOTALLY MARLOWE!..*

BUT...

SLEEZE BROTHERS P.I

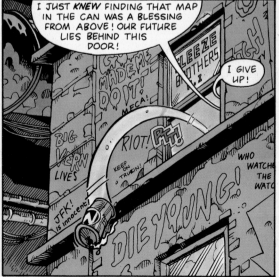

I JUST *KNEW* FINDING THAT MAP IN THE CAN WAS A BLESSING FROM ABOVE! OUR FUTURE LIES BEHIND THIS DOOR!

I GIVE UP!

OWW!

CLUNK!

WHAT THE ??

SERGEANT PIGHEADSKI... CAN MY MEN USE *UNNECESSARY* VIOLENCE TO HALT THE GANG WAR RAGING BEHIND US?

OF COURSE, OF COURSE! CARRY ON!

I SMELL SOMETHING *BAD* BREWING...

NOBODY...AND I MEAN *NOBODY* CANS A COP IN *MY* PRECINCT!

- SLEEZE... I SHOULD HAVE *KNOWN*!

DEADBEAT...WHAT IS THIS? HOW *COULD* YOU?

LOOK AT THIS PLACE, IT'S A *TIP!* EVEN THE *RATS* HAVE MOVED OUT! WHAT ABOUT MY *DREAM*, ALL THOSE YEARS IN THE RIM WARS... I USED TO VISUALISE THIS OFFICE...IT WAS THE *ONLY* THING THAT KEPT ME GOING!

NICE PLACE YOU GOT HERE, BOYS... SUITS YOU DOWN TO THE GROUND!

HUH! *PRIVATE EYES*...WELL YOU AIN'T GONNA BE DRUMMING UP A LOTTA DETECTIVE WORK FROM THE INSIDE OF A *CELL!*

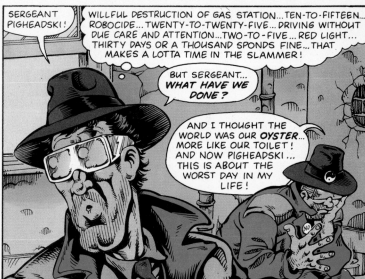

SERGEANT PIGHEADSKI!

WILLFUL DESTRUCTION OF GAS STATION...TEN-TO-FIFTEEN... ROBOCIDE...TWENTY-TO-TWENTY-FIVE...DRIVING WITHOUT DUE CARE AND ATTENTION...TWO-TO-FIVE...RED LIGHT... THIRTY DAYS OR A THOUSAND SPONDS FINE...THAT MAKES A LOTTA TIME IN THE SLAMMER!

BUT SERGEANT... *WHAT HAVE WE DONE?*

AND I THOUGHT THE WORLD WAS OUR *OYSTER*... MORE LIKE OUR TOILET! AND NOW PIGHEADSKI... THIS IS ABOUT THE WORST DAY IN MY LIFE!

YOU BOYS JUST CAN'T STAY OUT OF TROUBLE...YOU KNOW AS WELL AS I DO THAT *ILLEGAL DISPLACEMENT OF REFUSE* IS A MISDEMEANOR THAT CARRIES UP TO A *MONTH* IN THE PEN!

YEAH! YOU'RE GOING BACK WHERE YOU BELONG!

≡PHEW≡

BUT COME ON, SERGEANT...I'VE ONLY JUST GOT *OUT* TODAY...HAVE A *HEART!*

SLAM!

PIG!

HEY, DEADBEAT...THAT TIP YOU CALL AN OFFICE...IS THAT THE *BEST* YOU COULD DO? WHAT HAPPENED TO THE *MONEY*...THE *HIDDEN* MONEY?

EL APE... YOU ONLY GAVE ME *HALF* THE MAP...

...I ONLY GOT HALF THE MONEY!

DIRECTIVE ONE...YOU ARE UNDER ARREST FOR CONTRAVENING SECTION SIX, PARAGRAPH FOUR OF THE HIGHWAY CODE...RUNNING IN A BUILT-UP AREA...

THANK GOD...;PANT; ARREST ME ARREST ME...;PUFF; I WANNA SEE PIGHEADSKI...;PANT; I'M A BAD MAN!

DIRECTIVE TWO...YOU HAVE THE RIGHT TO REMAIN SILENT. ANYTHING YOU SAY MAY BE TAKEN IN COURT, AND USED AS...AS...ER...

EVIDENCE?

THAT'S IT- EVIDENCE! DIRECTIVE THREE...YOU HAVE THE RIGHT TO RECEIVE A SEVERE BEATING...AND A CUP OF MILKY TEA...

GET OUTTA MY WAY YOU MEATHEADS... OH NO..! YOU'VE LET HIM GET AWAY! YOU'RE IN BIIIIG TROUBLE NOW!

NO! FINKELLY... THE COPS HAVE GOT HIM...AND YOU'RE IN BIIIG TROUBLE..! THE COSMOS FATHER AIN'T GONNA LIKE THIS!

NO, NO...WAIT..! YOU DON'T HAVE TO TELL THE COSMOS FATHER! IT'S OKAY...I, I... I'VE GOT IT UNDER CONTROL...

I ER...I KNOW THESE TWO GUYS SEE...THEY'LL SORT IT OUT!

SLEEZE BROTHERS

IT'LL BE NO PROBLEM...

ANYTIME · ANYPLANET
ANYTHING!
206 LOWER CORE CENTRAL, BIG APPLE

THIS IS THE PLACE, DEADBEAT.

SURE IS, EL APE.

HMMM...

SHHHH!

OKAY... LET'S SYNCHRONISE WATCHES...

CHECK!

CHECK!

RIGHT.... LET'S DO IT!

17

18

19

LATER... THANK YOU, BOYS. YOU'VE DONE VERY WELL...

THERE YA GO, DEADBEAT... A HUNDRED SPONDULICKS FOR THAT LITTLE NUMBER. I TOLD YA BEING *PRIVATE DETECTIVES* WOULD PAY OFF !

EL APE!...THE CAMERA HIRE COST US *FIFTY* SPONDS... THE FILM *TEN*...AND THE SKELETON KEYS *FIFTEEN*...

YEP..! THAT LEAVES US *TWENTY-FIVE SPONDS*... AT LEAST WE'RE GONNA *EAT* THIS WEEK !

OH..! HELLO MR. COCKROACH!

SNATCH!

I'LL TAKE THAT , *SLEEZE*...AND IF I DON'T GET THE REST OF THE RENT MONEY YOU OWE ME *VERY* SOON, YOU'LL BE SLEEPING IN THE *GUTTER* WHERE YOU BELONG !

STUPID LITTLE ICEHOLES...

HEY, DEADBEAT...I'M NOT EVEN SURE HE CAN CHARGE RENT ON A *CONDEMNED* BUILDING !

EL APE...THIS IS A BUM RAP...WE SHOULDA STUCK TO SMALL-TIME VILLAINRY, WE WERE GOOD AT THAT !

AHH STOP *WHINGING*, DEADBEAT... *SOMETHING* WILL TURN UP... IN THIS TYPE 'A STORY, IT ALWAYS *DOES* !

AH, GENTLEMEN... COME IN...I'VE BEEN *EXPECTING* YOU!

HEY GET YOUR FEET OFF MY DESK YOU CHIPSUCKER... *DORIS!* WHAT'S THIS GEEZER DOING HERE? YOU'RE A *RECEPTIONIST*, YOU SHOULD'VE *STOPPED* HIM!

WHAT DO YOU EXPECT ME TO DO *FATHEAD*...I'M A *COMPUTER*...I'M *BOLTED* TO THE DESK....I CAN HARDLY KICK HIM IN THE GROIN AND TELL HIM TO COME BACK LATER!

DIGITALLY OPERATED RECEPTIONIST /SECRETARY 076

WHY YOU NO GOOD HEAP OF *SCRAP*...

I SHOULD *UNPLUG* YOU FOR GOOD...

YOU'RE ABOUT AS MUCH USE AS A *MATCH* IN *SPACE!*

BUT...BUT... SURE, EL APE... BUT...

YES, DORIS ...BUT...

HUH! IF IT WASN'T FOR ME... YOU'D GET *NOTHING* DONE!

YOU INCOMPETENT, UNGRATEFUL, FLATULENT *SLOB*...

AND WHEN WAS THE LAST TIME I GOT *SERVICED*... HEY...I BET YOU CAN'T *REMEMBER!*

SLAM!

IF YOU DON'T MIND ME *INTERRUPTING*...I THINK I'VE GOT A *CASE* YOU MIGHT BE *INTERESTED* IN!

Panel 1: WONG'S AIR BAR!

Panel 2: AH SO... MISTER SLEEZE AND MR SLEEZE! A HUNDRED THOUSAND WELCOMES...IT IS ALWAYS A PLEASURE WHEN YOU COME TO DRINK AT MY HUMBLE FRESH AIR BAR... *WHEN YOU PAY YOUR BILL!* ...WHERE'S MY MONEY YOU BACK-END OF A WINDY DRAGON?!

Panel 3: HEY, WONG...THERE'S NO NEED TO GET YER FURRY LITTLE BACK UP! JUST FEAST YA GREEDY, GUPPY EYES ON THIS!... I THINK IT'LL COVER MY TAB...FOR THE NEXT COUPLE OF MILLENNIUM!

Panel 4: MISTER SLEEZE, MR SLEEZE... FORGIVE MY SHORT-SIGHTEDNESS... THE FIRST DRINK IS ON ME!

Panel 5: SHOULDN'T WE BE LOOKING FOR CLUES, EL APE?

YA KNOW, DEADBEAT, I THINK YER *RIGHT*... BUT THERE'S AN OLD PRIVATE EYE SAYING THAT GOES LIKE THIS...'*KEEP YER EARS OPEN, YER EYES PEELED, YER NOSE CLEAN...* AND THE REST OF YA *FULL OF BEER!*

Panel 6: *FIFTY-SIX MACKLEBERRY'S LATER...*

MORE MACKLEBERRY'S FOR ME AND MY FREAKY FAIRWEATHER FRIENDS, WONG ≩HIC≩...AND ANOTHER GLASS OF *MILK* FOR MY LONG-SUFFERING SLEUTH-LIKE BROTHER HERE! ≩HIC≩

Panel 7: I'VE GOT ALL THE S-SPONDS WE NEED... WHOOPS!

25

NO UNAUTHORISED PERSONNEL BEYOND THIS POINT...YOU HAVE FIFTEEN SECONDS TO COMPLY... 15, 14, 13 ERR... 10

OKAY, OKAY! WE'RE *GONE*!

WELL, WELL, LOOK WHAT THE SEWERS THREW UP!... *SLEEZE P.I.*

TELL ME BOYS... WHAT DOES P.I STAND FOR? OH YEAH...I'VE GOT IT... *PATHETIC ICEHOLES*!

AHHH, *SERGEANT PIGHEADSKI*... NICE TO SEE YOU LOOKING SO *SMART*, GOING TO A *FANCY DRESS PARTY*?

CUT THE JIVE, SLEEZE,

OR YOU'LL BE PICKING PORK FROM YOUR PODGY FACE!

I WANT YOU TWO OUT OF HERE NOW, OR YOU'LL BOTH BE BACK IN THE *RIM WAR PENAL FORCES* BEFORE YOU CAN SAY *UNLAWFUL POLICE HARASSMENT*!

NOW BEAT IT!

SCUD..! WHADDA WE GOING TO DO NOW, DEADBEAT?

QUIT WHILE WE'RE AHEAD?

TAKE THE SPONDS AND RUN?

NOPE.

I GOTTA PLAN!

HELLO..! I'M *BELLE*, OF THE *BELLSTAR PHONE COMPANY*. PLEASE INSERT YOUR SPOND RATING, AND I'LL BE HAPPY TO MAKE YOUR CALL..!

THIS IS THE BELLSTAR VIDPHONE, MODEL 473352. IT'S GOT STATE OF THE ART, NEURO-TECHNICAL CAPABILITIES. IT'S *VANDAL-PROOF, TAMPER-PROOF, FIRE-PROOF, FALL-OUT-PROOF*, AND IT'S *WATER-RESISTANT* TO A DEPTH OF *FIFTY FATHOMS*...

GREAT!...THE LAST THING I NEED TO HEAR AT THIS POINT IN THE AFTERNOON, IS *YOU* EXPOUNDING THE VIRTUES OF A FRAGGIN' 'PHONE SYSTEM!

WHADDYA DOING WITH THAT *GUM*...STOP JERKING AROUND!

...BUT LIKE EVERYTHING IN THIS WORLD...IT'S GOT A *WEAK* SPOT..!

...YOU JUST GOTTA KNOW WHERE IT IS!

COME ON, DEADBEAT...GET *SERIOUS!*

PIECE OF GUM ON THE TELEOPTIC FIBRE...

...OLDEST TRICK IN THE BOOK!

THANK YOU FOR USING BELLSTAR...YOUR CALLS HAVE BEEN LOGGED.

THAT'S YOUR PLAN? SO *NOW* WE *SPLIT,* CUT OUR LOSSES AND GO GET TOTALLY *AIRED?*

JUST WAIT AND SEE!

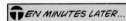 *EN MINUTES LATER...*

SEE!

I NEVER DOUBTED YOU FOR A MINUTE!

THIS IS GOING EXACTLY AS I PLANNED!

BIG TRUCKS
WHEN ONLY THE BIGGEST WILL DO

INTERSPERM

WHAT THE SCUD'S GOING ON HERE?

GET THIS JUNK OUTTA HERE!

I'M SORRY, BUT I'VE GOT A DELIVERY TO MAKE...SOMEBODY RANG AND ORDERED TWO DOZEN YUGWALIAN YUKKA PLANTS.

29

SOON...

YAKE YAKE YAKE

HAS ANYONE GOT A BUCKET?

CLONE SERVICE... WHO ORDERED FOURTEEN ROBERT REDFORDS?

WHERE DO YOU WANT THE SABRE-TOOTHED RHINO..?

PICK-A PET GENETIC ANIMALS

DANGER

YES, LIEUTENANT... NO, LIEUTENANT... RIGHT AWAY, SIR...

SSHH!

UH-OH!

AH, ER...HELLO...WE'RE FROM THE BELLSTAR PHONE COMPANY. PIG-HEADSKI SAYS THAT YOU SHOULD GO AND WATER THE GARDEN WHILE WE FIX THE PHONES...OKAY?

DIRECTIVE ONE...VACATE... OR BE ELIMINATED...YOU HAVE FIVE SECONDS TO COMPLY...4...3...

ER... DEADBEAT...

2... 1...

PIECE OF GUM ON THE OPTIC SENSOR...

SPLUDGE!

OLDEST TRICK IN THE BOOK..!

ZZZ ZZ

FRUMP!

30

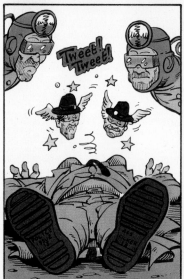

33

♪ HAPPY BIRTHDAY TO YOU... HAPPY BIRTHDAY TO YOU! ♪

WHAT THE...

YOUR *BROTHER* TOLD US TO GIVE YOU *THIS*...

WE FIGURED IT'S *GOT* TO BE YOUR BIRTHDAY RIGHT ..? THE WRAPPING PAPER AND SONG WERE *OUR* IDEAS...NO EXTRA COST...

HERE'S OUR CARD! THANK YOU, *GOODBYE!*

WOOSH!

HUH?

IN THIS WORLD OF CRIME, CORRUPTION, VICE, DOUBLE-DEALING, DRUGS, BACKSTABBING, ARSON, RAPE, LOOTING, SHOOTING, JAY-WALKING, PARKING ON DOUBLE YELLOW LINES...

ISN'T IT NICE TO KNOW YA CAN STILL BRING A LITTLE *HAPPINESS* INTO SOMEONE'S LIFE.??

IT RESTORES YER *FAITH* IN HUMANITY...LIKE...LIKE A TINY SINGLE FLAME CAN ILLUMINATE A CAVE THAT HAS BEEN *DARK* FOR *AGES!*

HEY, WAIT A MINUTE...I AIN'T *GOT* A BROTH...

KA-BOOM!

CONDEMED

DEADBEAT...

SOMETIMES I TALK A LOADA *SCUD!*

NIB NEWS

SICILLICON SUPERGRASS

TO TESTIFY AGAINST COSMOS FATHER

39

PEOPLE! PEOPLE! *PEOPLE!* IF ONLY *YOU* COULD SEE WHAT *I* CAN SEE WHEN I *GAZE* OUT OVER THE CITY WITH MY *ALL-SEEING* EYES! I SEE MY *DREAM* COMING *TRUE,* PEOPLE! *THAT'S* WHAT I SEE... I SEE *REEL-TO-REAL TV!*

HERE –*TODAY!* RIGHT IN THE ROTTING *CORE* OF THE *BIG APPLE,* MY FRIENDS, A SINGLE NETWORK WILL CORNER THE HOME ENTERTAINMENT SYSTEMS MARKET! YES, PEOPLE, THAT SINGLE NETWORK WILL BANKRUPT AND CRUSH IT'S RIVALS IN ONE *FOUL* SWOOP!

THAT NETWORK'S LOGO WILL BE FIXED ONTO THE EYEBALLS OF VIEWERS *ALL OVER* THIS WORLD, AND EVERY *OTHER* WORLD IN THE *GALAXY!*

YES!

YES!

YES!

YES!

THAT NETWORK WILL BE *OUR* NETWORK...THAT LOGO WILL BE *OUR* LOGO... *EN-EYE-BEE...* LET ME HEAR YOU *SAY* IT!

NIB!

NIB!

REEL-TO-REAL WILL BE *BIGGER* THAN THE NAR-COTICS INDUCTION BROTHERHOOD, WHICH GOT UP A FEW PEOPLE'S NOSES! IT'LL MAKE THE TAKINGS FROM THE *NUKEM* INVEST-MENT *BONDS* SCAM LOOK LIKE *A JUNIOR SAVINGS ACCOUNT!*

NIB!

NIB!

GENTLEMEN, WE'RE GOING TO BE *STINKING RICH!* AND WITH US TODAY, IS *THE* MAN WHO MADE IT *ALL* HAPPEN...

ORSUM WURLDS, THE GREATEST TV PRODUCER AND SYSTEMS DESIGNER THE WORLD HAS *EVER* SEEN... *YESSS!*

OH SMILER, DARLING...

IT WAS *NOTHING!* HONESTLY!

COME, *COME,* ORSUM...IS THERE *NOTHING* YOU WANT TO SAY?

WELL I WOULDN'T SAY NO TO A FEW MORE OF THESE *ROACH ROASTIES...* THEY'RE SIMPLY *DELICIOUS!*

HA HA HA! SO *MODEST!* THE *GREATEST* INVENTOR ON EARTH, AND ALL HE WANTS IS A FEW COOKED *BUGS! WURLDS'* YOU *ARE* A CARD!

CURSE THAT FAT CREEP, WURLDS! *REEL-TO-REAL* WAS MY INVENTION... *HE* STOLE IT FROM *ME*... I'LL I'LL...

AFTERNOON, *MR BAIRD*, IS THERE SOMETHING WRONG?

ER, NO! *NO!* I WAS JUST DROPPING SOME *PAPERS* OFF... I WASN'T LISTENING, OR SNEAKING AROUND OR ANYTHING, *HONEST!*

WELL, HAVE A NICE DAY THEN, AND REMEMBER, IF YOU HAVE *ANY* PROBLEMS, COME TO ME FIRST! WE DROIDS HAVE SPECIAL IN-BUILT CARING MECHANISMS..

JINGLE! JINGLE!

THIS IS THE *FINAL* STRAW, I WORKED MY BLOCK OFF GETTING REEL-TO-REAL TOGETHER AND NOW IT LOOKS LIKE I'LL END UP JUST LIKE THOSE DUMB STRIPEYS...

YES!

YES!

OH, YES!

JUST ANOTHER FACELESS, NAMELESS WORKER... IT'S *NOT* FAIR!

NOW CLOCK OFF

LAB

5:00

REEL & REAL TEST #509 ON LINE PROT MK 1

I'M GOING TO BE STUCK BACK HERE, IN THIS GROTTY LITTLE WORKSHOP, *BEHIND* THE SCENES *FOREVER!*

DURRR... HELLO, MR. BAIRD...

SHUT IT, GORD! GET THIS PLACE *CLEANED UP!* IT'S A *REAL* MESS!

ORSUM WURLDS

WHILE WURLDS *TAKES* ALL THE *CREDIT* FOR MY INVENTION... MINGLING WITH THE *STARS*... GETTING INVITED TO *PARTIES* WITH THE RICH AND FAMOUS... AND WHAT DO *I* GET!?!

ORSUM WURLDS

PROTOT MARK 1

NOTHING!

WELL I'LL SHOW *NIB* WHO THE *REEL* GENIUS IS... HA HA HA! YES! I'LL GIVE THEM A *REAL* RUN FOR THEIR MONEY! HA HA HA!

REEL & REAL MASTER TAPE NOT TO BE REMOVED

41

MEANWHILE...

EUREKA! I'VE GOT 'IM, DEADBEAT! ALL OUR PROBLEMS ARE SOLVED!

WOOPY-DOO!

COME ON, EL APE... THAT'S NOT MRS. PUDGEBUCKET'S PUMPLE...THAT, IS A SLUURRHUURRFFF, AND YOU KNOW IT!

AW, COME ON, DEADBEAT... IT'S PINK, FAT, AND FURRY – MRS. PUDGEBUCKET WILL LOVE IT!

PANT! PANT!

EL APE..! YOU WANNA TAKE THAT THING'S TONGUE OUTTA MY EAR WHILE I'M DRIVING?

DEADBEAT! THAT'S NOT ITS TONGUE...

MEANWHILE, AT THE HEADQUARTERS OF PURE MORAL TV...

BROTHERS AND SISTERS OF THE BOARD...WE ARE SOLEMNLY GATHERED HERE TODAY, BATHED IN THE GLORY OF CATHODE RAYS, TO DISCUSS A MATTER OF GRAVE IMPORTANCE!

THOSE HEATHENS AT NIB HAVE GONE TOO FAR THIS TIME...THEY ARE PUTTING THE SOULS OF THOUSANDS OF CITIZENS AT RISK!

THE SO-CALLED REVEREND SMILER WHILE IS NOW PLANNING TO ALLOW PEOPLE TO ENTER THEIR SICK TV WORLDS AS EXTRAS...! THIS COULD BE THE END OF PMTV AS WE KNOW IT! BUT, PRAISE BE, THE ALMIGHTY VIEWER UPSTAIRS HAS SENT AN ANGEL TO HELP US RID THE WORLD OF THIS SCOURGE... A BRAVE KNIGHT IN SHINING ARMOUR HAS JOINED US ON OUR HOLY CRUSADE!

MY FRIEND, HAS THE WRETCHED BUSINESS BEEN TAKEN CARE OF?

YEAH, YEAH, YEAH... IT'S DONE...

...WHERE'S MY MONEY?

AND NOW ON *NEXUS INFINITY BROADCASTING*, THE STATION OF THE NATION, IT'S TIME FOR THE VERY *FIRST* BROADCAST OF *REEL-TO-REAL TV*. SO ALL YOU LUCKY *RICH* PEOPLE OUT THERE, GET READY TO SWITCH ON, TUNE IN, AND *FREAK OUT!*

REEL to REAL

SPONSORED BY SEC COM ... RICH BANX INC ...

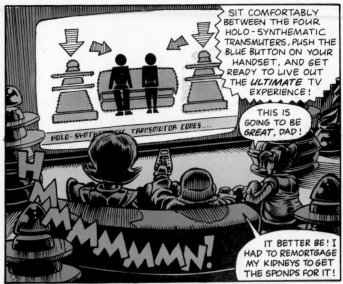

SIT COMFORTABLY BETWEEN THE FOUR HOLO-SYNTHEMATIC TRANSMUTERS, PUSH THE BLUE BUTTON ON YOUR HANDSET, AND GET READY TO LIVE OUT THE *ULTIMATE* TV EXPERIENCE!

HOLO-SYNTHEMATIC TRANSMUTOR CONES ...

THIS IS GOING TO BE *GREAT*, DAD!

IT BETTER BE! I HAD TO REMORTGAGE MY KIDNEYS TO GET THE SPONDS FOR IT!

HMMMMMMN!

AS A TRIBUTE TO CINEMATIC BRILLIANCE EVERYWHERE, WE'RE SHOWING A MEDLEY OF CLASSIC CULT CLIPS ... STARTING WITH *TOY WARS*, A SPACE NOVELTY!

ZOOM!

THE GUYS AT WORK'LL BE SICK!

WOW! TALK ABOUT *REAL!*

IT'S AMAZING ... I CAN'T WAIT TO TELL THE TOZARIANS NEXT DOOR! THEY'LL BE SO *GREEN!*

VOOSH!

LOOK, ZEEDY..! IT'S *BANDI*, THE OLD CARTOON CLASSIC!

YES, IT'S THE SCENE WHERE BANDI AND DUMPER ARE SKATING ON THE ICE!

CRRR AAAACK!

WHAT THE...

?

THIS WASN'T IN THE SCRIPT!

COME ON, DAD...REEL-TO-REAL STARTED *HALF AN HOUR* AGO!

OKAY, SON! LET'S SEE WHAT'S ON!

OH! IT'S THAT OLD FAVOURITE OF MINE... *TEN THOUSAND LEAGUES UNDER THE SEA!*

CLICK!

BLUB.. BLUB.. BLUB

NOT FAR AWAY... PIGHEADSKI...WE'VE GOT A SIX-FIFTY IN PROGRESS, 1644, WITHERING HEIGHTS... NEIGHBOURS REPORT MYSTERIOUS WATER LEAKAGE FROM APARTMENT... LIEUTENANT ROCKBOTTOM WANTS YOU TO CHECK IT OUT!

ROCKBOTTOM! WHAT DOES HE THINK I AM..?

A FRAGGING PLUMBER?!

SOON... THEY'RE *USUALLY* CLEAN AND QUIET... THAT'S WHY I CALLED, THERE'S DEFINITELY SOMETHING *FISHY* GOING ON!

OKAY, OKAY... DON'T TELL ME MY JOB! I'M THE POLICE OFFICER!

OPEN UP IN THERE... OR I'LL HAVE TO—

WHOOOSH!

THIS IS PIGHEADSKI... GET A MEAT WAGON DOWN HERE *FAST*...

...MAKE THAT A MEAT WAGON AND A *FISH MONGER*!

AT THE PUDGEBUCKET'S RESIDENCE... MRS. PUDGEBUCKET WANTS YOU TO *LEAVE* THE PREMISES, AND TAKE THAT EXCUSE OF A *PUMPLE* WITH YOU!

HEY— WHAT ABOUT OUR *EXPENSES*!

NOUVEUX REECH

GREAT IDEA, EL APE, NOW *WHAT*?

NO SWEAT, BRO'...

PANT! PANT!

THIS HEAP OF SLOBBER MUST BE WORTH SOMETHIN' TO *VINNIE THE VIVISECTIONIST*!

HEY! HERE, BOY! GOOD SLLUUURRHHUURRRFFY... COME BACK YOU FLEA HOSTEL!

HEY, EL APE, WAIT! WE'VE GOT A CALL!

AT N.I.B HQ... YOU CAN WIPE THAT GRIN OFF YA FACE, SMILER...WE'VE GOT *TWENTY* DEAD FAMILIES, *TWENTY* FRAZZLED-OUT REEL-TO-REAL SETS, AND WE'RE HOLDING *YOU* PERSONALLY RESPONSIBLE!

TWENTY COUNTS OF *TELECIDE*...BOY, IF I GET MY WAY, YOU'LL BE GOING DOWN FOR A LONG, LONG TIME!

NOW *COME ON*, SERGEANT... YOU'VE GOT NO *EVIDENCE* THAT THOSE WEREN'T *REAL* ACCIDENTS... SO LET'S NOT BE TOO HASTY!

REST ASSURED, I'M DOING EVERY-THING WITHIN MY POWER TO SORT OUT THIS LITTLE *GLITCH*!

YOU'D *BETTER* BE. I'M GONNA GIVE YOU TILL MORNING TO SORT THIS OUT!

BUT *I'LL* BE BACK...TO NAIL YOU IF YOU DON'T HAVE THE ANSWERS!

REEL-TO-REAL TV... *SCUD!* WHATEVER HAPPENED TO GOOD OLD-FASHIONED ENTERTAINMENT, LIKE *KILLBALL* AND *SPEAR CATCH?*

THE KIDS OF TODAY HAVE GONE *SOFT!*

THE SLEEZE BROTHERS!

OH *NO!* WHAT ARE *THEY* DOING HERE?

YOU KEEP OUTTA THIS YOU *BUNGLING*, NO-GOOD, CHICKEN-BRAINED *RETARDS!* I'LL, I'LL...

PIGHEADSKI...

...I WONDER WHAT HE WAS DOING HERE?

PERHAPS THEY'RE DOING A RE-MAKE OF *I MARRIED A FAT SLOB FROM OUTTA SPACE!*

AH! THE *SLEEZE* BROTHERS! COME IN, COME IN...A LITTLE SITUATION HAS ARISEN THAT REQUIRES YOUR *PARTICULAR* EXPERTISE! SIT DOWN AND LISTEN...

SOME TIME LATER...

HEY, I CAN'T BELIEVE IT... THAT WAS *THE* REVEREND SMILER WHILE... AND HE'S PICKED *US*, OUT OF THOUSANDS, TO SOLVE HIS CASE!

MUST HAVE BEEN A COMPUTER ERROR!

A *THOUSAND SPONDS* PLUS EXPENSES... AND WE START BY GETTING TO INTERVIEW NONE OTHER THAN *ORSUM WURLDS* HIMSELF!

I DON'T LIKE IT ONE BIT!

WITH THIS KINDA MOTIVATION, WE'LL SOON FIND OUT WHO'S TRYING TO RUIN THE REVEREND'S GOOD NAME!

SURE, AND PERHAPS WE'LL GET A *SCREEN TEST* WHILE WE'RE AT IT!

AHH - ENTER, ENTER...

YOU MUST BE THE TWO PRIVATE DICKS THE REVEREND'S HIRED TO SORT OUT THIS *GHASTLY* AFFAIR WITH REEL-TO-REAL!

YEP, THAT'S RIGHT, MR. WURLDS. I'M *EL APE SLEEZE*, AND THIS IS MY BROTHER, *DEADBEAT*.

WE'VE BOTH BEEN GREAT FANS OF YOURS SINCE OUR *AMATEUR DRAMATICS* DAYS...

PRIVATE DETECTIVES, EH? I WONDER HOW MUCH THEY KNOW!

WORKING LATE AGAIN, MR. BAIRD? HOW *CONSCIENTIOUS* OF YOU!

WE'RE GOING TO STRING HIM ALONG A BIT, AND GET HIM TO LEAD US RIGHT TO THE TOP... THEN WE'RE GONNA MAKE OUR MOVE!..

OH NO! THEY'RE ONTO ME..! I'VE BEEN RUMBLED!

RUSH, RUSH, RUSH... TUT! TUT! TUT! YOU'LL WORK YOURSELF INTO AN EARLY GRAVE, MR. BAIRD!

CAN IT, MOTORHEAD!

SECURIT

VISCONTI'S DAYS AS NUMERO UNO ARE NUMBERED! HE'S GONNA BE SO FULL OF LEAD PEOPLE WILL THINK HE'S A PENCIL!

HOW DID I DO, MR. WURLDS? DID YOU LIKE MY AD-LIBBING AT THE END THERE? HAVE I GOT THE PART?

I'M SORRY, YOU'RE JUST NOT TALL ENOUGH TO BE IN MY MOVIES...

...AND I HAVEN'T GOT THE FOGGIEST ABOUT THIS DAMN REEL-TO-REAL BUSINESS... I'M SORRY, I WISH I COULD HELP YOU...

THE SHUTTLE TICKETS AND FAKE PASSPORT ARE ON THEIR WAY OVER TO YOU NOW... I TRUST EVERYTHING IS OKAY YOUR END...

NO! IT'S NOT! TWO PRIVATE EYES ARE ON TO ME... I DON'T KNOW HOW... BUT DON'T WORRY, I'M GONNA TAKE CARE OF THEM TONIGHT!

AS USUAL, WE'VE GOT ZILCH! WHATTA WE GONNA DO NOW?

WELL, DEADBEAT, I ALWAYS THINK BETTER ON A FULL STOMACH!

FOUR SUSHI TAKE-AWAYS AND TWELVE CANS OF MACKLE-BERRYS LATER ≡ BLEURK ≡ I DON'T UNDERSTAND IT, DEAD-BEAT... WE WENT THROUGH EVERY OFFICE IN THAT BUILDING... AND WE STILL HAVEN'T GOT A CLUE!

PERHAPS WE SHOULD GO BACK IN THE MORNING WHEN THERE'S SOMEONE THERE!

MOO MILK

PEEP PEEP PEEP

HELLO, SLEEZE PI!

IF YOU WANT TO KNOW WHO SABOTAGED REEL-TO-REAL, MEET ME AT THE NIB RESEARCH AND DEVELOPMENT LAB, AT MIDNIGHT!

K-K-K!

WHO WAS IT?

OH, NOTHING, WRONG NUMBER!

BUT-IF MY RAZOR-SHARP INSTINCTS ARE RIGHT... I'LL BET WE'LL FIND ALL THE ANSWERS TO THE CASE AT THE NIB LABS AT MIDNIGHT!

THE SPIRIT

CYBERBETIN CALENDER

DON'T PANIC

RENT DUE NOW

MOO

GROOVY!

50

CUT THE CHATTER, YOU SLEEZES...THIS IS WHERE YOU GET *YOURS!*

WAIT! CAN'T WE WORK SOMETHING OUT? WE'VE GOT MONEY, *LOTS* OF IT, I'LL GIVE YA MY *WATCH...*

WOO! COPS AND ROBBERS... I LOVE WATCHING COPS AND ROBBERS!

BLAM BLAM

DERRR, IT MUST BE *GREAT* TO BE IN THE MOVIES!

ONTROL ROOM

PERSONNEL ONLY

CLICK!

WHIRR

REEL & REAL MASTER TAPE

MONTAGE

HEY! THE LIGHTS HAVE COME ON! WHO'S RUNNIN' THIS SHOW?

HHMMMMMMMMM MMMMMM!

WHAT'S HAPPENIN'?

BEATS THE HELL OUTTA ME...

HMMM MMMMMMMMMMM!

51

IN THE OUTSIDE WORLD, SLEEZE, YOU'RE THE BEST...BUT HERE, IN MY UNIVERSE... I AM SUPREME! HA HA! TALK ABOUT REAL!

I SPENT MY LIFE DEVELOPING REEL-TO-REAL... AND NOW I'M A PART OF IT... HA HA!.. I CAN BE ANYONE I CHOOSE... I CAN MANIFEST MYSELF AS THE VILLIAN OF THE PIECE FROM A CAST OF THOUSANDS!

SO...NOW YOU TWO KNOW THE TRUTH, NOW YOU KNOW WHO SABOTAGED REEL-TO-REAL...

WE DO?

...YOU MUST DIE!

HELP

CLICK!

WOOOOOEEEE!

DERR, MR. BAIRD'S IN THE MOVIES... HUHHAHA... OH GOODY, CARTOONS... I LOVE CARTOONS!

THOMAS?

WHU-WHERE ARE WE NOW... WHAT ARE WE DOING ON ALL FOURS ≡SQUEAK!≡... WHAT'S THAT CHEESY SMELL?

HEY, DON'T ASK ME, THESE SOCKS WERE FRESH THIS MORNING...≡SQUEAK!≡

DEADBEAT, ≡SQUEAK!≡ WHAT'S HAPPENED TO OUR *EARS?*

CLANG!

WUBBA WUBBA WUBBA

HA HA! I'LL GET YOU RATS ONE WAY OR ANOTHER!

THIS CAT'S *CRAZY!*

YEAH... HE'S BEGINNING TO CHEESE ME OFF!

GO ON, PUSSYCAT... SQUISH DOWS MICES TO PIECES!

CLICK!

WHIRR

REEL & REAL MASTERTAP

YUK..! THIS IS GETTING BEYOND A JOKE!

DEADBEAT..! I'VE *GOT* IT! WE'RE *INSIDE* REEL-TO-REAL TV!

YEAH, AND I KNOW WHAT FILM WE'RE STUCK IN!

WHAT?

IT'S *STRANGE, EXTRA-TERRESTRIAL LIFE FORMS, TWO!*

THIS IS THE REALLY GRUESOME BIT WHERE...

I DON'T WANNA KNOW!

SHLEAK

SHLOOPK

OUT OF THE FRYING PAN, INTO THE *FIRE!* HA HA HA!

FACE IT, SLEEZES... YOU'VE MET YOUR MATCH!

CUT! THE ACTING IN THIS IS TERRIBLE!

SCHLIK!

YOU'RE ALL FIRED!

FWOOSH!

SQWEEEEEEE

I DIDN'T KNOW YOU HAD A FLAME THROWER ATTACHED TO YOUR GUN, EL APE?

NO, NEITHER DID I! HEY, WHAT'S THAT HORRIBLE *HISSING?*

HISSSSSHH!

HISSSSS, NOBODY TORCHES MY KIDS AND GETS AWAY WITH IT!

OH, BROTHER...IT'S THE *MOTHER!*

55

HISS!

NOW. WHAT?!

QUICK! IN HERE!

HIS...!

HOW DID WE GET INTO THIS MESS?

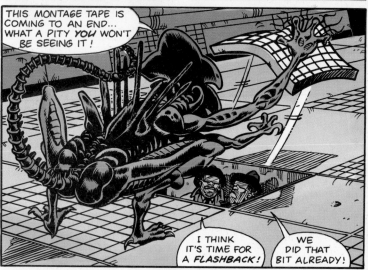

THIS MONTAGE TAPE IS COMING TO AN END... WHAT A PITY *YOU* WON'T BE SEEING IT!

I THINK IT'S TIME FOR A *FLASHBACK!*

WE DID THAT BIT ALREADY!

DEADBEAT, YOU'VE SEEN THIS MOVIE..! WHAT'S HE GOING TO DO TO US?

I DON'T KNOW... I LEFT BEFORE THE END!

LEAVE THEM ALONE, YOU BITCH!

HUH?

CLANK!

CLANK!

RIDLEY..? BUT, BUT...

56

GOOD EVENING, THIS IS *CATH ODE* WITH TONIGHTS *NIB NEWS*...REEL-TO-REAL T.V. HAS MADE THE HEADLINES AGAIN, AFTER POLICE UNCOVERED A CONSPIRACY TO SABOTAGE THE ALL-NEW, STATE-OF-THE-ART, SENSATION T.V...REASONABLY-PRICED AND AVAILABLE AT A GOOD HARDWARE STORE NEAR YOU!

MAJOR RATING RIVALS, *P.M.T.V* CONFESSED TO THEIR INVOLVEMENT IN THE SCANDAL, WHEN SENIOR MEMBERS OF THE BOARD DECIDED IT WAS THEIR DUTY TO SHOULDER THE RESPONSIBILITY, AND TAKE THE BLAME FAIRLY AND SQUARELY... OR ELSE SPEND THE REST OF THEIR DAYS GUILT-RIDDEN AND MISERABLE!

WE *CONFESS!* IT WAS *US! PLEASE*, PUT US INTO PRISON.

POLICE ARE NOW CONVINCED THAT *TOSHI BAIRD*, A NIB TECHNICIAN CORRUPTED BY P.M.T.V, UNWITTINGLY KILLED HIMSELF WHILST TAMPERING WITH REEL-TO-REAL'S HIGH-TECH MACHINERY...THUS EXONERATING THE SLEEZE BROTHERS...PRIVATE DETECTIVES BROUGHT IN BY NIB TO INVESTIGATE...

THEY SLIPPED THROUGH MY FINGERS THIS TIME! BUT I'LL GET THEM ONE DAY. YOU HEAR THAT *SLEEZE?*

I'LL GET YOU IF IT'S THE *LAST THING I DO!*

THE SLEEZE BROTHERS WERE UNAVAILABLE FOR COMMENT, AND WERE LAST SEEN HEADING EAST ON LOWER WACKER DRIVE IN THE COMPANY OF A FURRY CREATURE WITH AN UNPRONOUNCEABLE NAME...

EL APE, GET THAT THING *OFF* ME... *AAAGH!* IT'S DOING IT *AGAIN!*

STAY TUNED FOR THE REVEREND *SMILER WHILE*...COMING RIGHT UP AFTER THIS COMMERCIAL BREAK!

YO, T.V-TRIPPERS, SMILER HERE, BRINGING YOU GREAT NEWS. LAST NIGHTS TEST TRANSMISSIONS WERE SUCH A SENSATIONAL SUCCESS, THAT NIB HAS DECIDED TO GO *FULL-BEAM-AHEAD* WITH ITS PLANS! SOON *EVERY* FAMILY WILL BE ABLE TO BUY A SET!

ONLY $10,000 SPECIAL TRIAL OFFER!

THE CHOSEN FEW WHO TOOK PART IN LAST NIGHT'S TRIAL RUN SAID, "*IT WAS A ONCE-IN-A-LIFETIME EXPERIENCE!*' HA HA! JUST JOKING, FOLKS! SO I'LL BE SEEING YOU, AND REMEMBER...I'M ALWAYS WATCHING YOU, WATCHING ME, WATCHING YOU, WATCHING *REEL-TO-REAL T.V.*

A SNIP FOR THE TRIP THAT'S HIP!

THE BIG APPLE - THE HOME OF THE SLEEZE BROTHERS.

FROM THE UPPER CRUST, RIGHT UP AT THE VERY TOP, DOWN THROUGH PLATFORM ONE, AND THE STREET, TO THE SEWERS, WHERE THE MUTANT SCOOPERS LIVE, IT'S A CITY ROTTEN TO THE CORE.

MAGGOTS OF ALL SHAPES AND SIZES WRIGGLE THEIR WAY THROUGH THIS CITY, CHOMPING AWAY AT THE RIPE FLESH OF GOLDEN OPPORTUNITY. IT'S A WORLD OF BUG-EAT-BUG, A WORLD WHERE ANY TWO-BIT CREEPY CRAWLY CAN START AT THE BOTTOM AND EAT IT'S WAY UP TO THE TOP!

THIS IS NEVER MORE TRUE, THAN IN THE WORLD OF POLITICS...

SOMEWHERE OUT THERE, DEADBEAT, A CRIME HAPPENS EVERY 0.000333 OF A SECOND! IT'S A RICH BANQUET FOR ALL PRIVATE EYES TO ATTEND, AND WE'RE GOING TO GET OUR SLICE OF THE PIE!

YUP!

BLIP BLIP DIBBLEX

BLIP BLIP

THIS IS WHERE WE START OUR STORY: THE VERY HEART OF THE BIG APPLE, THE WHITE-WASH, FORTRESS OF PRESIDENT SINARTRA, A SMALL TIME EMBRYO FARMER MADE GOOD.

TODAY, SINARTRA IS THROWING A PARTY - AN UGLY BUG BALL - AS A BRAVE ATTEMPT TO RESTORE HIS FLAGGING POPULARITY AFTER THE EMBARRASSING 'ARMS FOR OSTRICHES' SAGA, WHICH SHOCKED THE WORLD!

TIME: 9·00

YET ANOTHER PARTY AND WE'RE STUCK OUTSIDE ON SECURITY AGAIN!

YEAH, IT'S NOT FAIR! THE EASTWOODS AND THE REYNOLDS ARE ALWAYS GETTING THE BEST SITUATIONS...

WHY CAN'T WE GO AND MINGLE WITH THE GUESTS? I MEAN, IT'S POINTLESS STANDING OUT HERE: THIS PLACE IS IMPENETRABLE...

SCHLEP!

SCHLEP!

SCHLEP!

SERVICE PERSONNEL ONLY

SCHLEP!

SKUTTLE SKUTTLE

SKUTTLE SKUTTLE SKUTTLE

AMBASSADOR GONK, SO NICE TO SEE YOU DARLING! I DIDN'T KNOW YOU STILL CAME TO THIS MISERABLE LITTLE PLANET...

OCCASIONALLY... IT'S SO QUAINT! BUT LET'S MOVE - HERE COME THOSE AWFUL SICILICONS!

BOSS, I HATE THESE PARTIES...

YOU JUST SMILE AND SHOW SOME RESPECT. THE PRESIDENT HAS BEEN VERY HELPFUL.

HEY, COSMOS FATHER, LET'S SPLIT! HERE COMES THAT PARANOID CREEP, HAIRDRYER...

SELLERS 114, I WANT THIS PLACE SECURE... THERE ARE PEOPLE EVERYWHERE!

THERE ARE SUPPOSED TO BE - IT'S A PARTY!

JUST DO AS I SAY! I'M THE HEAD OF THE GALACTIC INVESTIGATION BUREAU, NOT YOU!

THIS PARTY IS *AWFUL!* I'M GOING HOME!

I AGREE! WE HAVEN'T SEEN THE PRESIDENT ALL NIGHT!

THE PRESIDENT'S BEEN GONE AN AWFUL LONG TIME—SOMETHING MUST HAVE POPPED UP.

WITH MARILYN AROUND I'M NOT SURPRISED!

WILL THE PRESIDENT BE MUCH LONGER?

NO.

OH PRESSY WESSY... TELL LITTLE MARILYN WHAT'S UP...

WELL, IT'S THIS STUPID ARMS DEAL...AWW! THIS IS CLASSIFIED STUFF SWEETIE!

BUT PRESSY POOHS! IT'S NOT YOUR FAULT. YOU DIDN'T EVEN KNOW ABOUT THE OSTRICHES!

YES! NO! I ONLY DID IT SO THE PEOPLE COULD HAVE REAL ANIMALS IN THEIR ZOOS! THEN I WAS GOING TO MAKE A DEAL TO RELEASE SOME URBAN GORILLAS...

CLICK WHIRRR!

YOU'VE BEEN A NAUGHTY BOY—AND YOU KNOW WHAT THAT MEANS...

OH YES... YES! LOOSEN MY FANBELT, BABY PLEASE!

CLICK WHIRR RR!

...MORE OIL! MORE OIL!

CLINT 116—THIS IS HAIRDRYER! ANY TROUBLE?

QUIET AS A GRAVE, SIR.

DAMMIT! WRONG PIPE!

TIME: 9·20

...AND I CATERGORICALLY *DENY* THE *FILTHY*, SCANDALOUS RUMOURS BEING SPREAD BY CERTAIN SUBVERSIVE PARTIES ABOUT MYSELF AND THE GORG...ERR, *INTELLIGENT* AND *TALENTED* MS BLONDCLONE!

THE WHITEWASH...

"...CHEAP IMITATIONS OF *TWISTED* PERVERTS WILL *NEVER* BRING DOWN, BECAUSE I BELIEVE IN THE GREAT *CONSTITUTION* OF OUR BELOVED COUNTRY, 'LIBERTY, FRATERNITY AND *EGALITY*...'"

beep beep

J. EDGAR HAIRDRYER

CALL ON LINE FOUR, SIR!

WHO'S THAT?

IT'S ME, SIR, MISS JONES, YOUR SECRETARY...

JUST CHECKING - YOU CAN'T BE TOO CAREFUL NOWADAYS, SUBVERSIVES EVERYWHERE!

OKAY, PUT 'EM THROUGH...

RIGHT, YOU *PARANOID IMPERIALIST*, GET THIS; THIS IS THE *HUMAN LIBERATION FRONT*, AND WE *DEMAND* THAT YOU *ONE* — SEND US LOTS OF SPONDS SO WE CAN ARM OURSELVES TO THE TEETH...*TWO* — FREE ALL SPERMS THAT ARE BEING HELD AGAINST THEIR WILL IN YOUR FASCIST SPERM BANKS... AND *THREE* — GIVE US A *THOUSAND* THINGS WE HAVEN'T GOT ALREADY... *OR ELSE!*

OR ELSE *WHAT?*

HOW DO I KNOW YOU'VE GOT THEM?

OR ELSE THE PICTURES WE'VE GOT OF THE PRESIDENT AND BLONDCLONE WILL BE SPREAD ALL OVER THE FRONT PAGES OF THE *GUTTER PRESS!*

COPIES WILL BE ON YOUR DESK BY TOMORROW... AND IF THE FIRST OF OUR DEMANDS ISN'T MET BY THEN, THE PRESS GETS 'EM *NAZI SCUMBAG!*

9·33

DID YOU GET A *TRACE* ON THAT LAST CALL?

CALL, SIR? WHAT CALL? I'M ON LUNCH BREAK!

T.R.A.C.E.

T.R.A.C.E. = TELEPHONE RECONNAISSANCE AND COMMUNICATION ESPIONAGE...

LUNCH BREAK! THIS IS THE FRAGGING *SECRET SERVICE*, IF YOU WANT LUNCH BREAKS JOIN THE *CIVIL SERVICE!* WHAT KIND OF CHICKEN-SHACK OUTFIT DO YOU THINK THIS IS?

GET ME EASTWOOD 244, BRONSON 345, *NOW!* I WANT THOSE PICTURES FOUND!

YES, SIR, RIGHT AWAY, SIR...

TIME: 9·35

THE FIRST BLOW HAS BEEN STRUCK, BROTHERS! SOON, I, THE *GREAT MAN HUGH*, OR *HUSHMAN* TO MY FRIENDS, WILL LEAD THE *GREAT REVOLUTION*...

THE *HUMAN LIBERATION FRONT* WILL SEIZE POWER AND *REAL FREEDOM* WILL PREVAIL... NOW, ALTOGETHER... *FREEDOM OR DEATH, DEATH OR FREEDOM!*

RONDAL, THE PICTURES OF THE *PRESIDENT* AND HIS *BIMBO* SHOULD BE ON THEIR WAY TO US RIGHT NOW... SOON WE CAN PUT STAGE TWO OF MY *BRILLIANT* PLAN INTO ACTION!

DURR.RR, DOES THAT MEAN I CAN BLOW SOMETHING UP, HUGH?

YES, YES, YES!

WHERE IS THAT *BUGGER*? HE SHOULD'VE BEEN HERE AN HOUR AGO... HE'LL BE LATE FOR HIS OWN *FUNERAL*!

MAYALL MANO?

I PAID HIM WELL FOR THAT *DIRT* ON *SINARTRA*! HE'D BETTER NOT *DOUBLE CROSS* ME!

NOBODY DOUBLE CROSSES THE *GREAT MAN* HUGH!

RONDAL GET THE *VERY BIG* GUNS, WE'RE GOING ON A *BUG HUNT*!

HUGH! I'VE MADE YOU AND YOUR NICE LITTLE FRIEND SOME TEA AND BISCUITS!

ERR, NOT NOW, *MUMMY*... WE'RE JUST GO-ING OUT TO PLAY!

BE A GOOD BOY! COME HOME BEFORE DARK AND DON'T TALK TO STRANGERS!

YES, MUMMY... STUPID COW...

AAAH, THE KIDS OF TODAY...

SKUTTLE

SKUTTLE

9-40-HEADQUARTERS OF THE SICILICON MAFIA...

COSMOS FATHER, I HAVE SOMETHING YOU MIGHT LIKE TO SEE!

IT'S A *DRIVE-IN BUG*, THE LATEST HI-TECH *SPYING* DEVICE. EVEN THE *G.I.B.* HAVEN'T GOT ONE OF THESE LITTLE *BEAUTIES*!

ALL VERY WELL, *CANELONI*, BUT WHAT DOES IT HAVE TO DO WITH ME?

WELL, *PETRONI*, THIS ONE HAS BEEN MONI-TORING THAT *PATHETIC* REVOLUTIONARY GROUP, THE *H.L.F.*, AND WHAT IT HAS COME UP WITH MAY INTEREST YOU...

THE BUG IS AN *UGLY,* BUT USEFUL *FREAK* OF NATURE...

"ON IT'S HOME PLANET OF *VOYEUR MAJOR,* THE SHARP *SUPER EIGHT LENS* ON THE END OF ITS TAIL, LINKED VIA A *PHOTO-OPTICAL NERVE* TO THE COMPACT LAZER DISC *MEMORY BANK* INSIDE ITS BODY... "

"... HAS LITTLE OTHER USE THAN SENDING PLAYBACK SIGNALS DURING MATING SEASON TO ATTRACT A FEMALE... *LIGHTS PLEASE!*"

BUT IN THE RIGHT HANDS, IT CAN BE MADE TO REVEAL *ALL* THAT IT HAS SEEN AND HEARD IN THE LAST *TWELVE HOURS!* MAKING IT AN EXCELLENT AND VIRTUALLY *UNDETECTABLE* SPYING DEVICE!

THE PICTURES OF THE PRESIDENT AND HIS BIMBO SHOULD BE ON THEIR WAY TO US RIGHT NOW...

9·44 SO IT LOOKS LIKE THE *H.L.F.* HAVE GOT THEIR ACT TOGETHER AFTER ALL!

YES, AND IT SEEMS WE'RE NOT THE ONLY ONES THIS SO-CALLED *BUGGER* IS WORKING FOR!

I WAN'T YOU TO GET ME WHAT-EVER IT IS THEY'VE GOT, *CANELONI!* ANY EXTRA *DIRT* ON THE PRESIDENT WILL HELP US IN OUR... HOW CAN I SAY IT... *BUSINESS CAREERS!*

FIND THAT *H.L.F. BUG* AND ANY PHOTOS THAT EXIST OF THE PRESIDENT! I *WANT* THEM! OH, AND CANELONI, IF YOU COME BACK WITH-OUT THEM, YOU CAN CON-SIDER YOUR LIFE WITH-IN THE *FAMILY,* HOW CAN I PUT IT? AH, YES, THAT'S IT... *TERMINATED!*

SI, PETRONI!

SPLAT!

9·45... GREEBATOWN...

AH, YES, THAT'S IT... TERMINATED!

KLONCIONNY KONVSMONV SICILICONS!

KSOLVNN YCVKONNFF BUG!

XONY VVSNCO NINJA?

THUNK!

NINJA!?!

SIOK CIVNNV BIG TIME!

NOV NICNN YOU BET!

SOIVC NIFOLXS! HAI YA!

WELCOME TO GREEBATOWN X

C'MON LIL' PHONE...

bip bip diddley bip

JUS' ONE RING FOR UNCLE EL 'APE...

67

9·46... CENTRAL CORE, PLATFORM ONE...

♪♫♪

AAGHHHH!

?

♪♫♪♫

9·50...HEADQUARTERS OF THE *G.I.B.* IN THE AFFLUENT NUVEAU REACH DISTRICT...

REECH OB

GNOBS

G.I.B

FAST

HOLD IT, STOOLIE. NO-ONE COMES IN HERE WITHOUT A PASS!

SO WHERE DO ISE GET ONE?

INSIDE... *NOW* WHERE YA GOING?

INSIDE...

NOT WITHOUT A PASS YOU DON'T!

YOUSE TELL HAIRDRYER DAT DE STOOLIE'S HERE...OFF THE STREET WID INFO HE MIGHT BE INTERESTED IN!

I'M INTERESTED, STOOLIE... NOW SPILL THE BEANS!

DA WOID ON DA STREET HAS IT YOU GUYS IS LOOKIN' FOR AN ENTOMOLOGIST!

HUH?

SOMEONE WHO LIKES BUGS... AND I MIGHT JUST KNOW WHERE SUCH A GUY CAN BE FOUND!

WHAT DO YOU MEAN?

I'M A STOOL PIGEON, AND IF THE PRICE IS RIGHT, WE MIGHT BE ABLE TO DO BUSINESS!

OKAY. BUT YOU KNOW WE'RE GOING TO HAVE TO BEAT YOU UP FIRST?

SURE! I ONLY WORK WID PROFESSIONALS!

9·52...

NOT BAD FOR A HARD DAY'S GRASSING...

HEY, STOOLIE! WHAT ARE YOU DOING AROUND HERE? SINGING FOR YOUR SUPPER AGAIN?

DE GREAT MAN HUGH! HOW ARE YOUSE? YOUR MOTHER KEEPING WELL?

I WANT A WORD WITH YOU!

SORRY... GOTTA SPLIT!

DERRR... IS THIS THE ONE YOU WANT ME TO BLOW UP, HUGH?

BFNLOW FNUFF?!

NO, NO, RONDAL, I'M SURE OUR FRIEND AND ARDENT SUPPORTER OF THE CAUSE WILL VOLUNTEER ANY INFORMATION WE NEED TO KNOW WITHOUT US HAVING TO BLOW HIM TO BITS...

...WON'T YOU?

SURE! POWER TO THE PEOPLE!

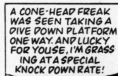

I WANT TO FIND AN ALIEN EAVESDROPPER CALLED THE BUGGER. HE HAS SOMETHING OF MINE... AND I WANT IT BACK!

I'LL TELL YOU WHAT I TOLD THE GOONS AT G.I.B...

A CONE-HEAD FREAK WAS SEEN TAKING A DIVE DOWN PLATFORM ONE WAY. AND LUCKY FOR YOUSE, I'M GRASSING AT A SPECIAL KNOCK DOWN RATE!

SMACK!

OKAY, YOUSE WIN... DAT ONE'S ON DE REVOLUTION!

9·53...

uurgh... fragging H.L.F... almost as bad as the sicilicons...

AW... ME AN' MY BIG MOUTH—

YANK!

HIYA, MR CANELONI! NICE TO SEE YOUSE!

BUTTON IT, STOOLIE, YOU WORM. TELL US WHAT WE WANT TO KNOW, OR THE BOYS WILL DANCE ON YOUR FACE.

9.50, PLATFORM ONE...

WOOooo

...AND NIGEL IN ACCOUNTS HAS BOUGHT HIMSELF A BRAND NEW FORD NEBULA XR4 I GHIA, RABBIT INJECTION TURBO PLUS GOLF TROLLEY!

NO! HOW DOES HE AFFORD IT ON HIS SALARY?

I KNOW... AND HE GOES SHOPPING EVERY NIGHT AT THE GETTY MALL!

CRACK!

OH B...

WOOoo

HE MUST BE DOING SOMETHING RIGHT!

YES, I KNOW!

SHUSSSHHHHHH

10.00...

SLEEZE PI

LOOK, RONDAL... UP IN THE SKY!

THE BUGGER! IF THE FALL DOESN'T KILL HIM, I WILL!

WELL, HE BETTER NOT SQUASH THE BUG WHEN HE LANDS.

I WONDER IF HE DOES HIS OWN STUNTS?

HEY, DEADBEAT, LOOK AT ALL THOSE PEOPLE POINTING UP AT US!

LOOKS LIKE OUR ADS ARE FINALLY PAYING OFF!

HMMM....

CRASH!

76

DE NIRO 124, SIR. ONCE AGAIN, THE PRESIDENT'S REPUTATION HAS ESCAPED UNTARNISHED. TRUTH, JUSTICE AND THE FREEDOM OF CHOICE HAS PREVAILED.

THAT'S BLOODY TYPICAL OF THE LOWER CLASSES... LYING DOWN ON THE JOB. OH WELL, THE REVOLUTION WILL HAVE TO WAIT... IT'S TEA TIME...

WE'LL SEND FLOWERS, CANELONI.

SCUD!

FINE! BYE BYE! CHEERS! DON'T WORRY ABOUT THE WALL! WE'VE GOT ANOTHER THREE ANYWAY! DROP BY ANYTIME! COME AGAIN! I'LL SUPPLY THE SLEDGE-HAMMERS! WE COULD HAVE A PARTY...

DEADBEAT! OUR OFFICE JUST GOT TRASHED AND ALL YOU DO IS SIT THERE PLAYING SPACE INVADERS ON THE STUPID COMPUTER!

DONE IT. WE'RE IN!

bip. bip. Ping!

MR. DEADBEAT, PARDON ME FOR BUTTING IN, BUT IT'S ILLEGAL TO TAP INTO THE FREELANCE INVESTIGATOR'S NEWS DIRECTORY UNLESS YOU'RE A FULLY PAID UP MEMBER...

SHUT IT, CHIP SUCKER! I'M TELLING HIM OFF!

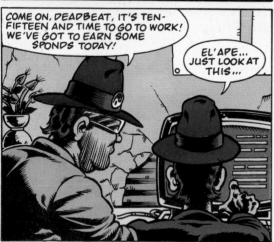

COME ON, DEADBEAT, IT'S TEN-FIFTEEN AND TIME TO GO TO WORK! WE'VE GOT TO EARN SOME SPONDS TODAY!

EL'APE... JUST LOOK AT THIS...

HEY! UGLY LITTLE SPUG! HE SHOULDN'T BE TOO HARD TO FIND!

UH-HUH.

WANTED

THE BUGGER. ALSO KNOWN AS THE BIG BUGGER. PLANET OF ORIGIN: UNKNOWN. WEIGHT: VERY LIGHT. VIOLENCE RATING: HARMLESS. LAST KNOWN WHEREABOUTS: FALLING. WANTED FOR INDUSTRIAL ESPIONAGE.

REWARD $20000

GO WARM UP HEINRICH, BROTHER! I'VE GOT A GOOD FEELING ABOUT THIS ONE!

EL'APE! TURN AROUND. THERE'S SOMETHING IMPORTANT ON YOUR DESK I WANT YOU TO LOOK AT!

IT'S HIM! THE BUGGER! SEE? WHAT DID I TELL YOU?! I KNEW WE'D FIND HIM!

YIPEE! 20,000$, AND WE HAVEN'T EVEN LEFT THE OFFICE YET! IT'S TOTALLY BOGART! WOW! IT'S GOING TO BE A GREAT DAY!

WHOOPIE-DOO!

As The World's Greatest Detective, you are invited to solve a "Murder in Space". Take the 6.15 shuttle to NORMAN'S FLOTEL. Dinner and Death at 8 pm. Signed: A. Mystery. R.S.V.P.

SAM SPUD. A MURDER IN SPACE SOUNDED PRETTY GOOD TO ME, SO I HOPPED ON BOARD THE SIX-FIFTEEN...

...I COULD TELL FROM THE INVITE THIS GIG WAS SOMEWHERE, A REAL FIRST CLASS CASE...

10

VANITY CASE. MURDER IN SPACE — REAL CUTE! JUDGING BY THE BRUTAL, SLASHING WAY THE T IS CROSSED IN THE SIGNATURE, I'D BET WE'RE DEALING WITH A HOMICIDAL MANIAC! HMMMM!

9 8

CHARLIE CHIN. THE UNIVERSE ITSELF IS A MYSTERY, AND MY LIFE IS BUT A MYSTIC ENTITY WITHIN THAT GREAT MYSTERY! NOW I HAVE RECIEVED THIS INVITATION SIGNED A. MYSTERY...

...THIS NOW BECOMES A MYSTERY FOR A MYSTIC WITHIN A MYSTERY!

7 6

MISS MC MUFFINS. MURDER, MURDER, MURDER! OOOHHHH, I LOVE A GOOD MURDER! I SHOULD HAVE THIS ONE SOLVED BY COCOA-TIME!

5 4

MIKE MALLET. ALL THIS FANCY FOOL TALK DON'T FOOL ME. THIS WHOLE THING SMELLS WORSE THAN A DOG WITH NO NOSE!

3

THE SLEEZE BROTHERS... WHAT A STROKE OF LUCK, DEADBEAT... FOOD, MUSIC, WOMEN, AS MUCH AS WE CAN DRINK, AND IT'S ALL FREE! THAT'S WHAT RSVP MEANS!

YEAH, THAT'S GREAT, EL 'APE, BUT FOR ONCE, JUST ONCE, I'D LIKE TO TRAVEL SEPARATE FROM OUR LUGGAGE!

2 1

...BLAST OFF!

KLUNK-
SSHHHH!

:BING BONG: PLEASE DISEMBARK VIA *AIRLOCK SEVEN*. THANKYOU FOR FLYING *PANGAL SPACEWAYS!* :BONG BING:

HA HA HA! HERE THEY COME... THE WORLD'S *GREATEST DETECTIVES!* UNSUSPECTING, LIKE *LAMBS* TO THE *SLAUGHTER!*

OOHHH! HELLO *MR. MALLET*, I HAVEN'T SEEN YOU SINCE THE *NEXUS CHAINSTORE MASSACRE...*

STILL DRINKING THAT *NASTY GREEBA HOOCH?*

YEP! OLD CHIN HERE SAYS IT'S GOOD FOR THE SENSES!

VERY VERY TRUE... IT MAKES ONE *INSCRUTABLE!*

VANITY... LONG TIME... *GASA-BLINKA 42.* GOOD TO SEE YA AGAIN. HOW ABOUT IT?.. YOU AND ME, JUST LIKE OLD TIMES.

I DON'T WANT TO *PLAY IT AGAIN, SAM,* SO JUST GET OFF MY *CASE.*

THERE IS AN OLD *GREEBA* SAYING: WHEN *FIVE* GREAT DETECTIVES GATHER TOGETHER, *TROUBLE* IS SURE TO FOLLOW!

HEEYYYY! NO NEED TO FEAR, THE *SLEEZE BROTHERS* ARE HERE! SO, PUT THE *MURDER* ON HOLD, THE *BEERS* ON ICE, AND LET'S *PARTEEEEEE!*

84

WU-WU-WELCOME TO NORMAN'S FLOTEL!

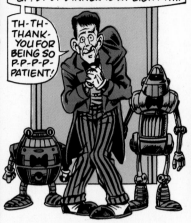

MY NAME IS N-NA-*NORMAN* N-N-*NORMALLER*, AND I AM YOUR M-M-*MC* FOR TONIGHT'S PROCEEDINGS! THE D-D-*DROIDS* WILL TAKE YOU TO YOUR ROOMS TO FRESHEN UP! DI- DI- DINNER IS AT EIGHT PM.

TH-TH-THANK-YOU FOR BEING SO P-P-P-*PATIENT!*

WHERE'S THE BAR? I NEED A DRINK AFTER LISTENING TO THAT!

I DON'T LIKE THIS ONE BIT! SOMETHING'S WRONG!

OF COURSE IT IS, MIKE, IT'S *MURDER!*

LATER... D-D-DINNER WILL BE SERVED SHORTLY, *MR. SPUD.* P-P-PLEASE TAKE A SEAT, W-W-WE'RE JUST WAITING FOR *MISS CASE.*

IT'S ALL *TOO* COSY FOR ME, I AIN'T GONNA BE SUCKED IN! I'LL SLUG THE FIRST ONE WHO TRIES ANYTHING FANCY!

SO YOU SEE, MISS MC MUFFINS, I GOT HERE THE SAME WAY AS YOU.

I DON'T CARE IF IT'S THE *WRONG* GLASS, JUST *FILL IT UP!*

AHH, YES! AN *INVITATION* — A BRILLIANT WAY TO GET US ALL HERE TOGETHER! WHOEVER THOUGHT OF IT IS A *GENIUS!*

SORRY I'M LATE... I HAD A LITTLE TROUBLE GETTING INTO MY DRESS.

MAAIIINN COURSE HAS ARRIVED! ≥WOOF WOOF!≤ ≥PANT PANT≤ ≥WHISTLE≤ BOY, OH BOY! WANNA SIT NEXT TO ME SWEETHEART?

DRY UP AND BLOW AWAY, *MAGGOT!*

SIR... SOUP IS SERVED.

ABOUT TIME TOO! I'M SO HUNGRY... I COULD EAT A SCOOPER!

Hmm... MY SUPER SLEUTH SENSES DETECT *PEPRONKA*! NO OTHER HERB GIVES OFF THE SAME AUTHENTIC SMELL OF BEEF LIVE-STOCK! THE CHEF CERTAINLY KNOWS HIS STUFF, EH, VANITY?

YOU COULDN'T BE MORE RIGHT, SAM. JUDGING FROM THE AL-MOST INVISIBLE SMEAR OF *SYNTHY-OIL* ON THE LIP OF THE PLATE, I'D HAVE TO ADD THAT THE CHEF IS A *ROBOCOOK 2000* — A TOP-OF-THE-RANGE *DELI-DROID*.

VERY GOOD, MISS VANITY, AND IN ALL HUMBLENESS, I WOULD LIKE TO ADD THAT JUDGING BY THE EXCELLENT TASTE OF THE SOUP, I CAN TELL THAT ALL THE VEGE-TABLES ARE FRESH, AND FUR-THERMORE, WE'RE PURCHASED BY THE CHEF, FROM *WU LING'S HOLISTIC GROCERY STORE, 144 YINGYANG WALK, GREEBATOWN!* THANK YOU!

Hmm... YES, I'D AGREE WITH YOU, CHIN, AND ADD THAT OUR DEAR ROBOCOOK HAS RECENTLY BEEN SERVICED BY ONE *WILL SPROCKET* — A FREELANCE *ROBOTECH*! WILL ALWAYS LEAVES THE RIGHT CALLIPER OF DROIDS IMPAIRED, TO BE SURE HE IS QUICKLY AND EXPENSIVELY RE-HIRED...

...HENCE OUR CHEF HAS MADE A SMALL CIRCULAR CHIP ON THE SIDE OF ALL OUR PLATES!

I DON'T GO IN FOR FANCY DE-DUCTIONS, BUT THE CHEF IS A ROBOCOOK WHO KNOWS HIS GAME, GETS HIS VEGETABLES FRESH, AND HAS A WONKY RIGHT ARM... BUT, WHAT YOU DIDN'T KNOW IS THAT HE HAS ONLY ONE GOOD LEG, A SHAT-TERED OPTIC SENSOR AND A HUGE DENT IN HIS HEAD!

OOOHH! HOW DID YOU KNOW ALL THAT, MIKE?

I PUNCHED HIM OUT BEFORE DINNER!

EL'APE?

SLURP!

BURP! IT'S OXTAIL... ISN'T IT?

DEF

THIRTY DEDUCTION-FILLED MINUTES LATER...

BURP!

I HOPE YOU ENJOYED THE M-M-MEAL! I HAVE BEEN INSTRUCTED BY A PERSON, OR P-P-PERSONS UNKNOWN...

...TO L-L-LOOK AFTER THE P-P-PROCEEDINGS, AND PLAY YOU THIS V-VI-VIDEO DISC...

...WHICH I'M SURE W-W-WILL ANSWER ANY Q-QU-QUESTIONS YOU MAY HAVE ABOUT W-W-WHY YOU ARE HERE!

YOU MAY BE WONDERING WHY YOU ARE HERE, THIS EVENING, SO I WON'T BEAT ABOUT THE BUSH... IT'S MURDER!

"WHAT MURDER?" I HEAR YOU ASK. YOU'RE MEANT TO BE SEVEN OF THE WORLD'S GREATEST DETECTIVES... YOU WORK IT OUT...

...AND BEFORE MORNING! YOUR VERY LIVES DEPEND ON IT! HA HA HA!

HA HA HA HA HA! CLICK!

I'VE HAD ENOUGH OF THIS SCUD! THERE AIN'T NO MURDER... THERE AIN'T EVEN A STIFF! I HAVEN'T COME ALL THIS WAY TO BE JERKED AROUND BY A VIDEO RECORDING!

EX-EX-EXCUSE ME, M-M-MISTER M-M-MALLET...

DROP DEAD, YOU STUTTERING, HUNCHEDBACKED FREAK!

CLUMP!

87

HAS HE FAINTED? I HARDLY TOUCHED HIM YA KNOW!

I'M AFRAID TO INFORM YOU, MR. MALLET, THAT MR. NORMALLER TOOK YOU LITERALLY!

WELL, THIS IS ONE MURDER THE BUTLER *DIDN'T* DO!

STOP JOKING ABOUT, YOU IMBECILE, THIS MURDER'S FOR *REAL!*

BUT HOW DID HE KILL POOR NORMAN?

NO SMELL OF POISON, NO SIGNS OF A HEART ATTACK... NOTHING! IN FACT, THE ONLY THING THAT SHOWS HE IS DEAD, IS THE COMPLETE ABSENCE OF *LIFE!*

IT'S AS THOUGH SOMEONE, OR SOME-THING, HAS JUST SWITCHED OFF HIS EXISTENCE LIKE A LIGHT!

OH GOODY, THE PLOT THICKENS!

RIGHT! SOMEWHERE ON THIS FLOTEL THERE'S A MANIAC WHO NEEDS *SHOOTING!*

WAY TO GO, MIKE, WAY TO GO...

...AND *WHILE* HE'S GONE, I THINK WE SHOULD GET POOR OLD NORMAN'S *WAKE* GOING... IT'S THE ONLY RESPECTABLE THING TO DO!

HOW CAN YOU TWO DRINK WITH A DEAD BODY IN THE ROOM?

JUST A QUICK LIVENER- TO GET THE OL' GREY MATTER GOING... CHIN RECKONS IT'S GOOD FOR THE CIRCULATION!

THAT'S RIGHT! ONE *STIFF DRINK*, AND NORMAN WOULD BE UP ON HIS FEET AGAIN!

AHHH, *CORVOSKY MEGA XXX* - THOSE EXQUISITE *GARG-ANTU GRAPES...*

BLAUGH AUGH AGH GH

DO YOU KNOW WHAT, ME DEARIES? I BET SOMEONE SLIPPED SOMETHING IN HIS DRINK!

TOO RIGHT, GRANNY, IT'S A *PIECE OF PAPER!*

THERE'S SOME KIND OF POEM ON IT... "SEVEN GREAT DETECTIVES LANDED IN A FIX, ONE DRANK SOME POISON WINE, AND THEN THERE WERE SIX!"

I PREFER *WORDSWORTH* MYSELF.

THE KILLER'S TAUNTING US... WE'VE GOT TO FIND HIM!

OOOHH GOODY! LET'S SEARCH THE BUILDING!

THAT'S RIGHT, YOU GO UPSTAIRS... WE'LL CHECK OUT THE *WINE CELLAR!*

ON SECOND THOUGHTS... DEADBEAT... LET'S GO AND CHECK OUT SOME BRIGHTLY LIT AREAS!

STOP *WHINING,* AND GET IN THERE!

DEADBEAT... THE KILLER COULD BE DOWN HERE, HIDING IN THE BLACKNESS WITH HIS GUN TRAINED ON US... WAITING TO KILL US. JUST WAITING...

POP!

AGGHHH! DIEEE CHIP-SUCKERRR!

BLAM!

POP!

SMASH!

BLAM!

CREESH!

BLAM!

BLAM!

TINKLE!

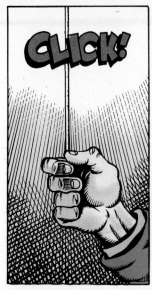

CLICK!

WHOOPS!

WELL, AT LEAST NO-ONE CAN POISON THE WINE NOW!

WHAT'S GOING ON? ARE YOU OKAY?

WE HEARD EXPLOSIONS!

CALM DOWN, CALM DOWN... IT WAS JUST THE WINE GOING OFF!

WE'VE SEARCHED THIS PLACE FROM TOP TO BOTTOM... IT'S *EMPTY*... WE HAVEN'T GOT A CLUE, AND UNTIL THE SHUTTLE ARRIVES IN THE MORNING, WE'RE STUCK HERE IN THIS SLAUGHTERHOUSE!

I'M AFRAID MISS VANITY'S RIGHT! WE ARE LIKE THE MAN WHOSE HOUSE HAS NO TOILET... WE HAVE NOTHING *TO GO ON!*

EEEEEEEEEEE

EEEEE

EEEEEEEE!

AAAEEEEEEEEEEEEEE

QUICK, IT'S MISS McMUFFINS— I'D RECOGNISE THAT SPINSTERLY SCREAM ANYWHERE!

THE TOILET, THE *TOILET!* IT'S *DISGUSTING!*

POOR OLD DAME, SHE CAN'T HANDLE THE *RICH FOOD!*

91

OH MY GOD!

YUK!

HOLY MANTRA!

GROSS!

IT LOOKS LIKE THE MANIAC HAS STRUCK AGAIN! MR MALLET IS *DEAD!*

WHAT A WAY TO GO! FLUSHED AWAY IN HIS PRIME TO THAT BIG *CESSPOOL* IN THE SKY! WHAT A *WASTE!*

ONCE AGAIN, THE KILLER HAS LEFT HIS CALLING CARD... "*SIX* GREAT DETECTIVES, GLAD TO BE ALIVE, ONE OF THEM WENT ROUND THE BEND, THEN THERE WERE *FIVE!*"

POOR MR MALLET! WE'VE GOT TO FIND HIS KILLER AND PUT A STOP TO THIS SENSELESS MASSACRE!

BUT *HOW?* WE'VE SEARCHED THIS PLACE FROM TOP TO BOTTOM, THERE'S NO-ONE IN THIS FLOTEL EXCEPT *US!*

PERHAPS THE KILLER'S HIDING *OUTSIDE!*

LET US LOOK AT THE SITUATION WITH THE MYSTIC OF *GREEBA!* WE ARE THE ONLY ONES ON BOARD THIS FLOTEL. NO-ONE CAN GET ON OR OFF, YES? I DOUBT VERY MUCH, MR SLEEZE, THAT SOMEONE IS HIDING IN THE GREAT VOID OUTSIDE. SO, AS EACH ONE OF US HAS HAD EQUAL OPPORTUNITIES TO COMMIT THESE DIABOLICAL DEEDS...

I WOULD SAY THAT THE ONLY LOGICAL CONCLUSION IS...

...THAT THE MURDERER IS *ONE OF US!*

DAN DAN NAN DAN DAAAN!

ZZZZZZZZZ ZZZZZZZ ZZZZZZZZZ ZZZZZZZZZ

COCKER DOODLE DOOOOOO!

NORMAN'S FLOTEL

WAKEY, WAKEY, MISTER SLEEZE! THE MORNING IS SURE TO DISPEL THE DARKNESS THAT DESCENDED ON US LAST NIGHT. I TRUST YOU ALL SLEPT WELL?

YEP! LIKE A *SLOTH* ON IT'S *FAVOURITE LOG!*

FINE, FINE! MISS McMUFFINS! WHERE'S MISS McMUFFINS?

SHE MAY NOT BE HEARING WELL! I'LL KNOCK AGAIN!

KNOCK KNOCK

MISS McMUFFINS... IT'S GETTING LATE—TIME TO GET UP!

SHE'S ALREADY UP!

HUH? BY THE BEARD OF BUBBA! SHE'S BEEN *HUNG* BY HER *OWN KNITTING!*

HUH? ANOTHER POEM... "FIVE GREAT DETECTIVES GO TO BED TO SNORE, ONE OF THEM DIDN'T WAKE UP. THEN THERE WERE FOUR!"

ONE OF US IS *REALLY* SICK! SOON WE'LL ALL BE DEAD—EXCEPT THE KILLER, THAT IS!

AFTER UNPICKING MISS MC MUFFINS FROM HER KNITTING... THE SHUTTLE WILL BE ARRIVING VERY SHORTLY! I SUGGEST THAT WE ALL JUST SIT TIGHT AROUND THIS TABLE, SO WE CAN KEEP AN EYE ON EACH OTHER!

tick tock

tick tock

tick tock

ANYONE FANCY A GAME OF *CLUEDO*?

IT WAS ONLY A SUGGESTION!!!

ALL THIS KILLING IS MAKING ME NERVOUS... I'M GOING TO THE JOHN!

AND WHERE DO YOU THINK *YOU'RE* GOING?

WE'RE COMING WITH YOU – FOR YOUR OWN SAFETY OF COURSE!

THIS *STINKS!*

TWENTY MINUTES LATER...

MISS VANITY! Hmm... VERY STRANGE! NOBODY SITS IN THE ROOM OF *METABOLIC TRANS-MIGRATION* FOR THAT LONG!

I DON'T LIKE IT!

KER-SMASH!

SHE'S *GONE!* VANISHED INTO THIN AIR!

LOOK ANOTHER *POEM!*

"FOUR GREAT DETECTIVES, ONE CALLED VANITY, GOD KNOWS WHERE SHE WENT, THEN THERE WERE *THREE!*"

THIS IS THE WORK OF DEVILS! WE ARE ALL DOOMED!

BUT THEY WON'T GET ME! AN OLD *GREEBA* SAYING SAYS...

...WHEN ALL THE OMENS ARE *FOUL* – MAKE LIKE A *CHICKEN!* I'M GOING HOME TO ROOST!

PTOOOOO

BACK IN THE DINING ROOM...

WE'RE THE ONLY TWO LEFT, DEADBEAT! SO, WHERE'S THE KILLER, EH? *WHERE*?

COME TO THAT, WHERE'S VANITY?

...AND SO YOU SEE, MISS VANITY, IT WAS ALL QUITE *SIMPLE!* KNOWING ABOUT THE *SECRET PASSAGES* WOULD HAVE SOLVED THIS MYSTERY...

...BUT NONE OF YOU CAME CLOSE TO FINDING THEM! HA! *GREAT DETECTIVES INDEED!* THE USE OF SECRET PASSAGES IS THE OLDEST TRICK IN THE BOOK!

AND, SWEET VANITY, IF YOU ARE WONDERING WHY I HAVE SPARED YOU...I WANTED SOMEONE TO WITNESS THE COMPLETION OF MY MASTER PLAN... AND...

IT'S AT TIMES LIKE THESE...

THAT A GIRL'S *MANICURIST* IS *DEFINITELY* HER BEST FRIEND!

...AND... AND... GOSH! I JUST *REALLY* FANCY *YOU!*

AHH! YOU CREEP!

MEANWHILE...

DEADBEAT! WE CAN'T JUST STAND AROUND WAITING FOR THE KILLER TO SHOW UP!

CLICK!

WOOOAHH!

98

IT WAS *ME!* I DID IT! I AM THE MURDERER! I AM *JACQUES* — NORMAN'S *PARASITIC BROTHER!* HA HA HA!

UG-LY!

I HAD A HUNCH IT WAS HIM ALL ALONG!

MOCK MY APPEARANCE IF YOU WILL, BUT I POSSESS A RAZOR SHARP MIND STRONG ENOUGH TO CONTROL ALL THE ACTIONS OF MY WEAK-WILLED HOST, NORMAN!

YOU THOUGHT NORMAN HAD DROPPED DEAD, BUT IN HIS STATE OF CATATONIC SHOCK, THAT I INDUCED, HE WAS MY PERFECT ACCOMPLICE! UNKNOWING, HE HELPED ME BUMP YOU OFF, ONE BY ONE!

BUT NOW, MY LAST VERSE! "TWO GREAT DETECTIVES LEFT ALL ALONE, WE COMMITTED ALL THE MURDERS AND THEN KILLED OURSELVES, THEN THERE WERE NONE!"

KILLED?

uhnn...

THAT'S *RIGHT!* WITH ALL YOU *HANDSOME* DETECTIVES GONE, I CAN RELAUNCH MY CAREER AS A P.I. PEOPLE WILL HIRE ME DESPITE MY LOOKS, BECAUSE I'LL BE THE WORLD'S *ONLY* DETECTIVE! TIME FOR YOU TO DIE!

N-N-N-

WELL, WE GOT THAT SORTED, DEADBEAT.

YUP. ANOTHER MYSTERY SOLVED.

LET ME OUT, SLEEZE! I'M WARNING YOU!

THUMP THUMP

I DON'T KNOW HOW, BUT WE ALWAYS SEEM TO COME OUT ON TOP OF THE CASE!

SLEEZE! SLEEEEEZE!

WE JUST WAIT FOR THE SHUTTLE, TELL THE AUTHORITIES HOW WE SOLVED THE CASE, COLLECT THE REWARD AND THE GLORY...

THEN REMEMBER THAT VANITY'S STUCK IN THE CUPBOARD!

NICE PLAN.

zzzzzzz

EXTRA

SIGN of the TIMES

MURDER IN SPACE!

VANITY UNVEILS VILE VILLAIN

EXTRA

...THAT VANITY SURE HAS A MEAN TEMPER, DEADBEAT!

YUP. AND SHE'S STRONG TOO!

DAMAGED GOODS

DESTINATION: SPACE DUMP

YOU KNOW WHAT, DEADBEAT?

WHAT?

THE BUTLER DID IT AFTER ALL!

WAAAAGHHHHHHHH

DADDY, DADDY, FIDO BIT ME!

NOUVEAU REACH

GEEZUS! THEY NEVER SAID IT COULD DO THAT AT THE PET SHOP!

DADDY, DON'T FLUSH IT, IT'S GOT TEDDY!

SPLOSH! GROWL SPLUTTER

DON'T WORRY, DARLING, I'LL GET YOU A NEW TEDDY.

BUT TEDDY'S GOT MY ARM AS WELL!

GUPLUSHHH!

BUT, FOR AN INDEFATIG-ABLE MONSTER THAT NEVER SLEEPS, IT'S GOT A SUPRISINGLY DELICATE STOMACH! THE DIGESTIVE SYSTEM OF THE BEAST IS A HIGHLY BALANCED MECHANISM. IT TAKES THE ENDLESS FLOW OF AFFLUENT EFFLUENCE FROM THE UPPER-CRUST AND PLATFORM ONE...

... AND FILTERS AND CHANNELS IT ON ITS LONG JOURNEY DOWN TO THE BOWELS OF THE CITY...

EVERYTHING POSSIBLE IS RECYCLED... THAT'S WHY THE WATER ON THE STREET TASTES SO BAD!

AND WHAT REMAINS IS LEFT FOR THE SCOOPERS — STRANGE COPROGENERIC MUTANTS...

BAA SPLOOSH!

...WHO ACT LIKE INTESTINAL JUICES-DEVOURING EVERY-THING!

NOOK! DOVER DARE, A NABBAGE!

SPLISH

SPLOSH

SLISHISLOSH! DRIP DRIP

LOVELY-NOTTEN RIGHT FREW!

NEY! NOT'S NAT NOISE?

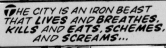

FOLLOWING LAST WEEK'S DISAPPEARANCE OF THREE MAINTAINANCE MEN...

WILL YA LISTEN TO THAT *BILGE, DEADBEAT!* NEXT THEY'LL BE TELLING US THERE'S A *MONSTER* LOOSE IN THE SEWERS!

EL'APE, WHERE'S THAT GODAWFUL CASE FILE?

NOT NOW, BROTHER, I'M TRYING TO LISTEN TO THE NEWS. BESIDES, WE ALL KNOW *MR. GODAWFUL* DID IT... HE'S *GUILTY!*

...EYEWITNESS, *MR. B. LURDVISION,* CLAIMS TO HAVE SEEN A HUGE, SLOBBERING MONSTER...

EL'APE, YOU CAN'T *CONDEMN* A MAN JUST BECAUSE HE'S GOT *BUCK TEETH, CROSSED EYES, A BIG NOSE, STICKY-OUT EARS* AND *GINGER HAIR!*

WHY NOT?

OTHER NEWS... THE STARS ARE ALREADY GATHERING IN TOWN FOR TOMORROW'S ANNUAL *PHONEY AWARDS,* HOSTED BY NONE OTHER THAN *PRESIDENT SINARTRA* HIMSELF! A LARGE CROWD HAS APPEARED OUTSIDE THE *DOOBEY DOO WAP PLAZA HOTEL,* HOPING TO CATCH A GLIMPSE OF THE LOVELY *MS. MARILYN BLONDCLONE,* WHO'S STRONGLY FANCIED TO WIN THIS YEAR'S AWARD...

...IF SHE PULLS IT OFF AGAIN, SHE GETS TO KEEP THE ZILLION CARAT PHONEY FOR GOOD... LET'S TAKE A LOOK AT A CLIP FROM HER LATEST MOVIE, *SILICON VALLEY...*

HUH, SHE'S BOUND TO WIN- IT'S A FOREGONE CONCLUSION. EVERYONE KNOWS THAT SHE AND *SINARTRA* ARE BED BUDDIES!

SHE LUBRICATES HIS FANBELT, AND *WHAMMO,* SHE PICKS UP THE AWARD FOR *BEST FEMALE NON-ALIEN CLONE ACTRESS IN A SUPPORTING BRA!* BOY, SOME PEOPLE SELL OUT SO EASILY, AND WHAT FOR?

I'LL TELL YA WHAT FOR... *MONEY!* THEY MAKE ME SICK!

beep

EL'APE, THE PHONE!

beep

HELLO, *SLEEZE P.I....*

YOU'VE GOT TO HELP ME... I'M A DESPERATE WOMAN... I NEED YOUR HELP!

AH, *MS. BLONDCLONE,* I WAS JUST SAYING WHAT A BIG FAN OF YOURS I AM! HOW CAN I HELP YOU?

I'VE BEEN SO STUPID. FOR NEARLY FIVE YEARS, THE *PHONEY* HAS BEEN SAFE IN MY POSSESSION, AND NOW I'VE GONE AND LET IT GET *STOLEN,* :SOB: IF I DON'T GET IT BACK BEFORE THE AWARD CEREMONY, TOMORROW, I'M FINISHED!... MY CAREER WILL BE OVER! :SOB SOB:

DON'T WORRY, MA'AM, ME AND MY BROTHER ARE *EXPERTS* AT TRACING STOLEN GOODS. YOU JUST GO AHEAD AND KNOCK 'EM DEAD AT THE CEREMONY, WE'LL GET THE PHONEY AND MEET YOU THERE!

OH, HOW CAN I EVER THANK YOU?

CLICK!

PURRR PRRRR

THEY'D BETTER FIND IT BEFORE ANYONE ELSE DOES! THAT PHONEY CONTAINS MY INSURANCE POLICY. WITH IT, THE PRESIDENT *HAS* TO KEEP ME IN THE LIFESTYLE I'M ACCUSTOMED TO! HAHAHA!

CHOKCXK

SO MUCH FOR YOUR PRINCIPLES, EL 'APE!

YEAH!

MY PRINCIPLES CAN ONLY BE OVER-RIDDEN BY MY CODE OF ETHICS, AND THEY SAY NEVER LEAVE A DAMSEL IN DISTRESS...

...ESPECIALLY A RICH, FAMOUS AND WELL-STACKED DAMSEL!

HUH! PIG!

LET'S THINK... A STOLEN PHONEY! WHO'D FENCE SOMETHING THAT HOT?

LENNIE THE PALM?

HE'S IN POKEY! WHAT ABOUT *KLEPTOMUS MAXIMUS*?

HE'S DEAD! *JOHNNY FINGERS*?

HE'S A TROMBONIST! WE'RE LOOKING FOR A THIEF WHO'S BIG ENOUGH AND UGLY ENOUGH TO FENCE HIS OWN STUFF!

RIGHT!

EXCUSE ME!

EXCUSE ME!

WHAT ABOUT THE *FROG BURGLAR*?

DIGITALLY OPERATED RECEPTIONIST/SECRETAR

OF COURSE — *THE AMPHIBIAN EMPORIUM!* THE FROG BURGLAR'S SO LOW AND SLIMY, HE'D SELL SCUD TO A SCOOPER!

LET'S BOOGIE!

SLAM!

MY PROGRAMMER WARNED ME ABOUT USERS LIKE THOSE!

THE AMPHIBIAN EMPORIUM IN THE HEART OF THE BIZARRE...

WELL, FREDDO, DID YOU COME UP WITH THE GOODS?

THIS QUEUE'S A NIGHTMARE!

INDEED, INDEED, ⨀RIBBET⨀ JUST AS I PROMISED, BUT THERE'S BEEN A SLIGHT CHANGE OF PLAN! THE ORIGINAL PRICE WE AGREED ON WILL HAVE TO BE RE-NEGOTIATED!

WHY YOU DIRTY DOUBLE CROSSING TOADRAG!

HOW PERCEPTIVE OF YOU, MR. HAIRDRYER... DOUBLE IS EXACTLY WHAT I WAS THINK-ING OF!

I DON'T KNOW WHY I HIRED YOU IN THE FIRST PLACE, YOU WART-COVERED, FLY-EATING FREAK!

TUT TUT! COMPLI-MENTS WILL GET YOU NOWHERE!

NOW, WHEN WILL I GET IT?

YOU'LL BE GETTING IT SOON ENOUGH, BUT IN THE MEAN TIME YOU'D BETTER MAKE SURE THAT THING'S SAFE OR ELSE! ⨀CLICK⨀

HUR HUR HUR!

HA HA! IT COULDN'T BE SAFER! ⨀RIBBET⨀

SCUZZ, RETRIEVE THE GOODS!

I'M TRYING, I'M TRYING... NOW, WHERE DID I PUT IT? ER, BEHIND THE STEREO? OR WAS IT THE VIDEOS? AH-HA! THERE IT IS BEHIND THE PACK-ING CRATES!

⨀RIBBET⨀ I DON'T KNOW WHY MR. HAIRDRYER FINDS THIS CHEAP AWARD SO ATTRACTIVE!

BUT I DO KNOW THE PRICE FOR ACQUI-RING IT FOR HIM WILL KEEP US IN SWAMP WATER FOR LIFE!

SO, THE FROG BURGLAR THINKS HE CAN CHEAT ME, THE GREAT J. EDGAR HAIRDRYER- HEAD OF THE G.I.B.? WELL, THE LITTLE TADPOLE'S OUT OF HIS DEPTH! HE'S SWIMMING IN THE BIG POND NOW! I'LL HAVE HIS LEGS BROUGHT TO ME ON A PLATE!

MISS LEY, GET ME AN OLIVET SERIES 2000!

WELL, AS YOU CAN SEE, WE HAVE ALL MANNER OF GOODS FOR SALE FROM THE LICIT, TO THE *NOT SO* LICIT!

I'M SURE YOU'VE GOT WHAT I WANT, SOMETHING THAT GLITTERS, BUT IS NOT GOLD...

... A PRIZE NOT WORTH WINNING, SOMETHING FAKE...

SOMETHING *PHONEY!*

UMMM, *RIBBIT:* THIS IS A SPECIAL REQUEST INDEED! I'D BETTER TAKE A LOOK IN MY STOREROOM AND SEE IF I CAN LOCATE THIS ITEM... *SCUZZ*, COME WITH ME.

YES, MASTER, ER HUR HUR!

WHOEVER THEY ARE, THEY'RE ON TO US! I'LL KEEP THEM TALKING *RIBBIT:* YOU GRAB AS MUCH SWAG AS YOU CAN AND MEET ME ROUND THE FRONT IN THE *FROGMOBILE.*

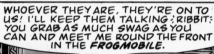

YETH, MARTHER! *SPLUTTER*

I'M SORRY, GENTLEMEN, BUT SOMEONE SEEMS TO HAVE ALREADY PAID A *DEPOSIT* FOR THE ARTIFACT YOU DESIRE. *RIBBIT:* CAN I INTEREST YOU IN SOMETHING ELSE?

NOPE! OUR BUSINESS IS *FINISHED*... AND SO ARE *YOU*, FLYSUCKER!

HEY! YOU CAN'T JUST PUSH IN LIKE THAT!

GET TO THE BACK, *BIG EARS!*

QUEUE JUMPER!

OUCH

CRASH!

SMACK

I THINK YOU KNOW WHAT I'M HERE FOR. GIVE IT TO ME NOW. OR THERE'LL BE... *TROUBLE!*

TROUBLE?

HE BROKE MY NOSE!

I'LL KILL 'IM!

WHO DOES HE THINK HE IS?

SECTION HOUSE THIRTEEN... THIS IS *GOLDEN RETRIEVER* TO KENNEL CLUB. QUARRY HAS GONE TO GROUND. THIS UNIT HAS SUSTAINED *MINOR DAMAGE* DURING HUNT. AWAIT FURTHER DIRECTIVES, OVER.

MESSAGE RECEIVED, *GOLDEN RETRIEVER.* NEW DIRECTIVES ARE AS FOLLOWS... *SIT, STAY, BARK* WHEN QUARRY MOVES, *FETCH THAT STICK!*

RECEIVED AND UNDERSTOOD. I WILL BE A *GOOD BOY.* OVER AND OUT!

THAT'S WHAT I LIKE, A REAL *PEDIGREE* EMPLOYEE... *PATRIOTIC, FAITHFUL, OBEDIENT,...* WHY I'D BET HE'D *FETCH MY SLIPPERS* IF I ASKED HIM TO. HMM... IT'S A PITY ALL MY STAFF AREN'T *ROBOTS!*

INSIDE THE STY...

SCRATCHINGS... THIS WHOLE THING SMELLS WORSE THAN A *SCOOPER'S JOCKSTRAP,* BUT I CAN'T FIGURE IT OUT. THE *FROG BURGLAR'S* KEEPING HIS TRAP SHUT TIGHTER THAN A *SNAKE'S SPHINCTER!*

HUH! I'D GET MORE SENSE FROM A *FRIDGE!*

HOW ABOUT INTERROGATING THE *SLEEZES,* SERG?

...AND THAT LEAVES US WITH *SCUZZ.* LET'S HOPE THE LITTLE CREEP IS THE WEAK LINK IN THE CHAIN, OR WE'VE GOT NOTHING. OPEN IT UP!

OKAY, SCUZZ, TIME TO SPILL THE BEANS!

WE CAN DO THIS THE EASY WAY... OR THE *HARD* WAY!

HUR, HUR, HUR! I AIN'T TELLING YOUS NOTHINK, YOU BAD EXCUSE FOR A *BACON JOINT!*

NOW YOU LISTEN TO ME, YOU PIECE OF *ALIEN SPACE JUNK!* IF YOU DON'T START TALKING FAST, MY BOOT'S GONNA PUT YOU BACK INTO *ORBIT* WHERE YOU BELONG!

NOUCH! NILE DALK. NILE DALK. NET GO OV MY DOSE.

IT WOZ DE **FWOG**. HE SNOLE IT... HIRED NYE SOMENUN BIG.

WHAT THE HELL ARE YOU TALKING ABOUT?

YOWCH! CRIME DOESN'T PAY **WELL ENOUGH** FOR THIS! I'LL TELL YA EVERY-THING I KNOWS. JUST LEAVE ME **NOSE** ALONE!

ONE NASAL CONFESSION LATER...

OKAY, WHERE'S THIS **PHONEY** THEN?

IT'S IN HIS MOUTH WHERE HE KEEPS ALL HIS LOOT!

WHAT?

SCRATCCCHIIIIINGSSSS! OPEN UP THE FROG'S CELL. HE'S GOT THE **EVIDENCE!**

NO NEED TO OPEN UP THE **CELL**, SIR, HE'S BEEN IN THE **JOHN** FOR THE LAST TEN MINUTES... SAID SOMETHING ABOUT **CONSTIPATION!**

CONSTIPATION?

OH NO — **THE EVIDENCE!**

STOP THAT **PLOP** IN THE NAME OF THE **LAW!**

HAHA! ⸰RIBBIT⸰ NO PHONEY, NO EVIDENCE!

NO EVIDENCE — NO **CASE!** HA HA! ⸰RIBBIT RIBBIT⸰

SO, THE EVIDENCE HAS **SLIPPED THROUGH MY FINGERS!**

YOU'RE GOING NOWHERE UN-TIL I'VE BEATEN **SEVEN BUCKETS** OF **SCUD** OUT OF YOU... YOU STINKING NO GOOD...

So... LET ME GET THIS STRAIGHT. IF WE DON'T GO DOWN INTO THE SEWERS AND GET THE PHONEY WITHIN *FOUR HOURS,* YOU'LL THROW THE BOOK AT US!

CORRECT! YOU'LL BE CHARGED WITH RIOTING, INCITEMENT TO BLASPHEMY, JAYWALKING, AND FOR WEARING UNSAVOURY CLOTHING IN A PUBLIC PLACE DURING DAYLIGHT HOURS!

AND THAT ADDS UP TO?

LIFE!

OKAY, DEADBEAT, LET'S GO!

GROOVY!

·RIBBIT· IF THEY FIND THAT PHONEY, I'M FOR THE *HIGH JUMP...* BUT PERHAPS THOSE IDIOT DETECTIVES COULD LEAD ME TO IT?

AND DON'T GET ANY SMART IDEAS WHEN YOU'RE DOWN THERE... I'LL BE *WAITING!*

GOLDEN RETRIEVER TO KENNEL CLUB... QUARRY HAS BOLTED. THE *HUNT* IS ON!

TRACK AND RETRIEVE. I *WANT* THAT TROPHY! TERMINATE ANY HUNT SABOTEURS WITH *EXTREME PREJUDICE!*

Down Below...

DEADBEAT. WHAT'S HAPPENING DOWN THERE? CAN YOU SEE ANYTHING?

SNOPE. DUFFING!

WHAT'S WITH THE FUNNY VOICE?

WELL, DEADNEAT, I'LL NEDDER MOAN ABOUT ABOUT NOR SOCKS AGAIN.'

HOW DOES PIGHEADSKI EXPECT US TO FIND THE PHONEY IN THIS MAZE?

JUST FOLLOW ME BROTHER, I'VE GOT A *NOSE* FOR THIS TYPE OF THING!

OUR FATHER, WHO ART IN HEAVEN... GET US THE HELL OUT OF HERE!

RRAAAARRRGHHH

HUH?

YIP! YIP!

THE FROG BURGLAR!

SPROING

YELP!

BLAT!

I THINK THIS BELONGS TO ME! THANK YOU FOR LEADING ME TO IT. ~RIBBIT~ I COULDN'T HAVE DONE IT ON MY OWN! HAHA!

LOOK OUT...

BEHIND YOU!

HUH, 'BEHIND YOU'... THAT'S THE OLDEST TRICK IN THE BOOK!

GRAWLSLOBBER!

CHOMP!

GRAWLSLOBBER!

WE'RE **DOG MEAT**, PAL. DEADBEAT, DOOOOO SOMETHINGGGG!

GRAWL!

♪♪♪

DEADBEAT! HOW DID YOU DO THAT?

IT WAS NOTHING. JUST A LITTLE TRICK I PICKED UP FROM MY PET-MINDING DAYS!

GRAWL Yip Yip Yip!

THIS LITTLE CREATURE'S A **MORIVIAN MORPHMAULER**. CUTE, BUT HOMOCIDAL WHEN RILED.

MIRACLE.

POOHVERS.

DIRTY DEITIES.

UNTIE THEM.

GOD-TAMERS.

⊙NE BAD BANQUET LATER...

TAKE NIS TNUNNEL, IT GNOES TO THE DOOBEEDOO PLAZA.

CHEERS, **POTEE**, I'LL THINK OF YOU, EVERYTIME I USE THE **JOHN!**

WE'VE GOT **FIFTEEN MINUTES** BEFORE THE SHOW. IT'S A LONG CLIMB, BUT WE COULD STILL DELIVER THE PHONEY ON TIME!

YUP, AND COLLECT THE MONEY SHE OWES US!

I THINK YOU'VE GOT WHAT I WANT. HAND IT OVER, OR THERE'LL BE **TROUBLE!**

TROUBLE? OH NO...

HERE, TAKE IT! WE'RE GOING TO FIND YOU AND GIVE IT UP ANYWAY, WEREN'T WE DEADBEAT... **DEADBEAT!**

♪♪♪

GRAWLLLLL!

I'M. IN. **TROUBLE.**

CHOMP!

SEE, DEADBEAT, *THAT'S* WHY WE'RE SUCH COOL DETECTIVES, WE NEVER GO TO PIECES AND *LOSE OUR HEADS!*

YUP.

SLURP!

ONE IMPOSSIBLY LONG JOURNEY LATER...

...AND THE WINNER IS... *MARILYN BLONDCLONE*, FOR HER OUTSTANDING BITS IN *SILICON VALLEY!*

CLAP CLAP CLAP

PUFF PANT!

CONGRATULATIONS, MARYLYN, I'VE ALWAYS ENJOYED YOUR MARVEL-OUS PARTS, ERR... AND SO FOR WINNING THE AWARD *FIVE CON-SECUTIVE* TIMES, YOU GET TO KEEP THE PHONEY *FOR GOOD!*

THE PHONEY... WHERE'S THE PHONEY?

WHERE'S THAT *OLIVET*?

WHERE ARE THE SLEEZES?

LADIES, GENTLEMEN AND SMALL FURRY, GREEN THINGS, I, *EL'APE SLEEZE*, PRIVATE EYE EXTRAORDINARE, AM PROUD TO BE HERE TONIGHT, IN PERSON, TO PRESENT THIS AWARD TO *MISS MARILYN BLONDCLONE!*

CLAP

OMIGOD!

THANK GOD!

WHAT'S HAPPENING?

OMIGOD!

OMIGOD!

WHAT'S HAPPENING?

FUNNY PLACE TO KEEP A FILM! STILL, CAN'T HAVE BEEN IMPORT-ANT... OHH, THEY'VE GONE ALL WHITE!

I KNEW IT. SHE'S BEEN TAKING PICS OF THE PRES IN COMPROMISING POSITIONS! THAT ICEHOLE'S RUINED MY EVIDENCE!

DAMN! THERE GOES MY INSURANCE POLICY ON SINARTRA!

YIPEE, LET'S HEAR IT FOR THE SLEEZE BROTHERS!

THIS JUST GOES TO SHOW, FOLKS, THAT WE'VE GOT GOOD OLD REGULAR STYLE HEROES RIGHT HERE IN THE BIG APPLE!

COME HERE, BOYS, I WANNA SHAKE YOUR HANDS!

SHUCKS! IT WAS NOTHING REALLY!

WELL, IN THAT CASE... GUARDS, GET THEM OUTTA HERE... THEY SMELL BAD!

HEY, WAIT A MINUTE...

AND SO, THE SHOW MUST GO ON...

YOU NO GOOD, TWO-FACED PHONEY! HOW COULD YOU DO THIS TO US? WE COULDA' BEEN STARS!

EL'APE... THAT'S SHOWBIZ!

THIS IS TYPICAL, DEADBEAT. HOW COME WE ALWAYS END UP WITH NOTHING?

WE'VE GOT THE MORPH-MAULER!

YOU MEAN YOU WANT TO KEEP HIM?

IF HE FEEDS MAINLY ON CROOKS, HE WON'T COST MUCH TO KEEP, AND HE'D MAKE AN EXCELLENT GUARD DOG! WHAD'YA SAY EL'APE?

WELLLLL...

HE IS KINDA CUTE!

HUH, CAN WE KEEP HIM THEN, HUH?

SLURP!

NAAAAAA! GOD BLESS YA!

#YIP?

HE'S BETTER OFF IN THE SEWERS. AFTER ALL, HE'S A GOD DOWN THERE... HE'LL BE ROLLING IN IT!

YUP. SNIFF SUPPOSE SO!

THAT REMINDS ME, WHAT ABOUT PIGHEADSKI? HE'LL BE WAITING FOR US TO COME UP!

NAAAAA! THAT WAS OVER TEN HOURS AGO. NOBODY CAN BE THAT STUPID!

TAP TAP TAP

IT'S A *MESS*, THAT'S WHAT IT IS...

THAT'S NO SHOOTING STAR, *THAT'S* A *SPACESHIP!*

NO-ONE COULD HAVE SURVIVED THAT!

GOING DOWN

WOO-WOO WOO-WOO

JUGS!

SLEEZE BROTHERS

ANYTIME · ANYPLANET
ANYTHING!

URGHHH... YOU'VE GOT TO HELP ME... THE FATE OF THE GALAXY DEPENDS ON *YOU!* YOU MUST DELIVER...

SLEEZE BROTHERS P.I.

THE ...MALTEEZE EGG!

I AM QUARKVARK, THE... URGGHHHH!

WUMP!

HEY, I DON'T CARE **WHO** YOU ARE, YOU CAN'T JUST BARGE IN HERE AND BLEED ALL OVER OUR CARPET.

HELP ME PLEASE.

GO AHEAD, DEAD-BEAT, LET'S TURN THIS PLACE INTO A HOSPICE FOR EVERY SICK AND DYING ALIEN WHO HAPPENS TO BE PASSING!

I AM **QUARKVARK** FROM THE PLANET **MALTEEZIA**, A PLANET THAT KNOWS NO WAR, A PLACE OF PEACE AND HARMONY, AND ALL THANKS TO ONE MAN ...

"...THE **TRUE MESSIAH**. THROUGH HIS WISDOM WE HAVE RISEN ABOVE THE STUPIDITY OF CONFLICT, AND HAVE ATTAINED **THE WAY**."

"WE HAVE PROPAGATED THIS PEACE TO MANY PLANETS, AND NOW, ONLY THE **RIM WARS**..."

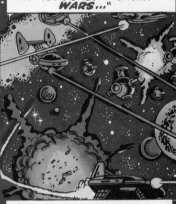

"...FUELLED BY THE UN-SCRUPULOUS ARMS DEALERS, STAND BETWEEN US AND ETERNAL PEACE."

"IT WAS TO THIS GREAT PROB-LEM THAT THE MASTER TURNED ALL HIS POWERS..."

"...FOR TEN YEARS, HE SAT ABOVE THE GREAT **PERCEPTION PYRAMID OF PONGO**..."

"...FINALLY, IT CAME TO HIM - THE MESSAGE THAT WOULD END ALL WARS. NOW HE WOULD CON-VEY HIS ENLIGHTENMENT TO THE **FIVE THOUSANDTH GALACTIC CEASEFIRE MEET-ING**, ABOUT TO BE HELD HERE ON EARTH."

"WE SET OFF IN TWO SECRET SHUTTLES - ONE CARRIED MY-SELF, THE MESSIAH AND A CO-PILOT, THE OTHER, HIS MOST **DEVOUT DISCIPLES**."

"BUT ALAS, THERE WAS A JUDAS AMONG US, THE SECRET CO-ORDINATES OF OUR HYPERSPACE RE-ENTRY HAD BEEN TAMPERED WITH..."

"... WE APPEARED, ALONE, INTO THE MIDST OF A MERCENARY AMBUSH. SOMEONE DIDN'T WANT THE MESSAGE TO GET THROUGH."

- YAWWWNN - DON'T STOP, THE SUSPENSE IS KILLING ME!

"OUR SHIP WAS FLEET AND WE MANAGED TO OUT-MANOEUVRE OUR ASSAILANTS..."

"... THEN, JUST AS WE WERE ABOUT TO ENTER THE EARTH'S ATMOSPHERE, WE SUSTAINED A DIRECT HIT, WHICH KNOCKED OUT OUR ENGINES..."

KA-BOOM!

"...AND SENT US CRASHING DOWN, BLAZING LIKE A COMET!"

"THE CO-PILOT DIED INSTANTLY, AND THE MESSIAH WAS MORTALLY WOUNDED, BUT IN THOSE LAST MOMENTS HIS WILL TO SHARE THE MESSAGE WAS STRONGER THAN EVER. BEFORE HE DIED, HE UNDERWENT THE MYSTIC PROCESS OF TEMPORAL TRANS-MIGRATION..."

"... HE TRANSFERRED HIS BRAIN WAVE PATTERNS INTO THE MOST IMMEDIATE SOURCE OF RETENTIVE PROTOPLASM..."

... WHICH HE FOUND IN MY LUNCH BOX. THE MESSIAH IS DEAD, BUT THE MESSAGE LIVES ON WITHIN THE FRAGILE SHELL OF THIS EGG!

I THINK HIS BRAIN'S GOT A BIT SCRAMBLED ON THE WAY DOWN.

NO! YOU MUST LISTEN. YOU'RE MY ONLY HOPE. THE PEACE OF THE GALAXY NOW DEPENDS ON YOU! TAKE THE EGG TO THE WIMP * BUILDING AND SEEK OUT THE DHARMA-LAMA... HE WILL KNOW WHAT TO DO!

* WARDENS OF THE INTERGALACTIC MISSION OF PEACE.

WHAT D'YOU TAKE US FOR, EH... A COUPLE OF ROOSTERS? HUH! A MESSAGE THAT WILL SAVE THE GALAXY INSIDE AN EGG... WHERE DID YOU HATCH THAT ONE FROM?

PLEASE... JUST DO AS I SAY. ALL THE WARING FACTIONS WAIT UNDER A FRAGILE CEASEFIRE FOR THE MESSAGE... IF IT'S MONEY YOU WANT, TAKE THIS MEDALLION... IT'S GOLD! ≶URGGG≶ THEY'LL BE PLENTY MORE WHERE THAT...≶URGGG≶

GOLD? WELL WHY DIDN'T YOU SAY SO IN THE FIRST PLACE? I'VE ALWAYS WANTED TO SAVE THE GALAXY!

KAFF! KAFF! URRGHHH—

LET'S GO AND GET BREAKFAST TO CELEBRATE EVERLASTING PEACE. I JUST KNEW FROM THE MOMENT YOU STUMBLED IN THAT...

EL'APE...

... WE WERE GONNA BE GREAT BUDDIES!

EL'APE...

WELL, HOW WAS I TO KNOW HE WAS DEAD?

RANGE   SCOPE   AXIS

I RECKON THAT GUY WAS A FRUITCAKE... BUT GOLD MEDALLIONS ARE GOLD MEDALLIONS, SO LET'S CHECK IT OUT!

FIRST, THOUGH... BREAKFAST TIME!

HOW CAN YOU EAT AT A TIME LIKE THIS? IT'S ONLY SEVEN THIRTY!

MORNING, ALI, WHAT'S COOKING?

FOR YOU, MR SLEEZE... EGGS VINDALOO A LA NATURELLE!

HUH?

RAW CURRIED EGGS!

JUST A BURGER PLEASE, ALI.

EL'APE, PUT THE EGG SOMEWHERE SAFE!

DON'T WORRY, BRO', IT COULDN'T BE SAFER!

TARGET ENGAGED.

THOOM!

EL'APE! YOUR LACE!

FWOOOOOOEEEE!

THANKS, DEADBEAT, THAT COULD HAVE BEEN NASTY...

IF WE TAKE THE EXPRESSWAY TO *NIXON AVE*, PICK UP THE *HEINZZ FREEWAY*...

... COME OFF AT THE *RONALD ROUNDABOUT*, CUT THROUGH *DEELY-BOPPER PLAZA*...

ZUMMMM

ZIK ZAK ZONG... HICKY BIK BOK... THERE THEY GO...

...OVER *WOODY ALLEN QUAY*, THEN DOWN INTO *LIBERTY SQUARE*, WE'LL BE THERE IN NO TIME!

EL'APE, WE'RE BEING FOLLOWED!

I THINK WE SHOULD TAKE A LEFT!

AWW, COME ON, DEAD-BEAT, THAT DYING ALIEN HAS GOT YOU SPOOKED!

TAKE A LOOK BEHIND US!

GRRR

BRRMMMM

ZUMMM

OKAY! LET'S TAKE A LEFT!

134

137

138

142

WHOOPS!

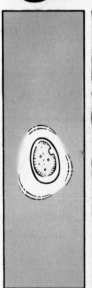

SPLUT!

THERE GOES THE GALAXY...

HANG ON A MINUTE, BROTHER... IF THEY WANT AN EGG, I'LL GIVE THEM AN EGG!

LOOKS LIKE IT'S THEIR LUCKY DAY!

TEN MINUTES LATER...

THANK YOU... THANK YOU! THE DHARMALAMA IS UNDERGOING TEMPORAL TRANSFER, AND SOON THE SECRETS HELD WITHIN THE EGG WILL BE KNOWN TO ALL! SURE YOU WON'T STAY AND SEEN IN A NEW ERA OF PEACE?

THANKS... BUT WHEN YOU'VE SEEN ONE PEACE, YOU'VE SEEN 'EM ALL!

144